The Institute of Biology's
Studies in Biology no. 118

Social Behaviour of Animals

John M. Deag

B.Sc., Ph.D.
Lecturer in Zoology, University of Edinburgh

D1569456

Edward Arnold

First published 1980
by Edward Arnold (Publishers) Limited
41 Bedford Square, London WC1B 3DQ

British Library Cataloguing in Publication Data

Deag, John M
    Social behaviour of animals. – (Institute of Biology.
    Studies in biology; no. 118 ISSN 0537-9024).
    1.   Social behaviour in animals
    I. Title   II. Series
    591.5   QL775

    ISBN 0-7131-2770-8

Printed and bound in Great Britain at
The Camelot Press Ltd, Southampton

General Preface to the Series

Because it is no longer possible for one textbook to cover the whole field of biology while remaining sufficiently up to date, the Institute of Biology has sponsored this series so that teachers and students can learn about significant developments. The enthusiastic acceptance of 'Studies in Biology' shows that the books are providing authoritative views of biological topics.

The features of the series include the attention given to methods, the selected list of books for further reading and, wherever possible, suggestions for practical work.

Readers' comments will be welcomed by the Education Officer of the Institute.

1980   Institute of Biology
                                                     41 Queen's Gate
                                                     London SW7 5HU

Preface

A major contemporary theme in the study of social behaviour has been an attempt to understand the forces that determine its nature. For example, why are there so many different types of animal groups (even among closely related species) of varying size, permanency and composition? Why do animals differ so markedly in the nature, context and frequency of their social behaviour? Why do they compete or cooperate?

To answer these and similar questions requires an integrated approach: (1) careful studies of behaviour are combined with those of ecology, physiology, population dynamics and population genetics; (2) comparisons are made between different types of animals (closely or more distantly related), different populations and different habitats; and (3) evolutionary studies are used to suggest how natural selection may operate on social behaviour.

This Study depends largely on bird and mammalian examples. In such a brief account it is undesirable to treat equally all facets of the subject, but the reader will find many of the gaps filled by other, more specific, Studies in this Series.

It is necessary to thank those whose work has been used for examples and to thank the following colleagues for helpful comments on the manuscript: Professor A. Manning, Dr N. P. Ashmole and Dr M. Dow.

Edinburgh, 1980   J. M. D.

Contents

1 Social Behaviour

1.1 What is social behaviour?

Social behaviour is behaviour involving two or more animals. The examples used here will involve members of the same species: but students may later like to consider whether the term social behaviour should be used to include interactions between members of different species.

Social behaviour and communication All social behaviour involves *communication*, which is the passing of any information from one animal to another by means of signals that have evolved for the purpose. We judge that communication has occurred when one animal's behaviour alters the probability of another animal's behaviour. The information passed between animals is typically a statement about the environment, the signaller's physiology or its intentions. For example, by giving a characteristic call on sighting a domestic cat a blackbird (*Turdus merula*) signals the danger to its mate and young; by presenting her bottom to a male, a female monkey indicates her readiness to mate. Understanding communication is central to the study of social behaviour and it is examined more closely in Chapter 5. Other examples of social behaviour include a male bird singing from a song-post when establishing its territory; a mammal suckling her young and two domestic dogs snapping at each other while disputing for a female in heat.

Social interaction Animals do not continuously interact socially. Even those that live in societies have periods of solitary activity during which they move, feed, preen or rest. These *maintenance activities*, involving little direct communication between individuals, are often punctuated by vigorous social behaviour. A feeding starling (*Sturnus vulgaris*) may be interrupted by another attacking and chasing it from a food item, a kittiwake (*Rissa tridactyla*) resting on its ledge immediately becomes active as its mate returns or a neighbour lands on an adjacent ledge. Such distinct bouts of social behaviour are called *social interactions*. We must be careful not to confuse our terminology. 'Social' is *not* being used here in the sense of 'for the common good'. We tend to think of fighting or threatening behaviour in people as 'anti-social'. In our present context these are legitimate examples of social behaviour. 'Social behaviour' is an all-embracing term. Unlike feeding behaviour, sexual behaviour and parental behaviour, social behaviour refers not to a specific category of behaviour, but to all of the ways in which animals influence each other.

Social 'instinct' The expressions 'social instinct' and 'gregarious instinct' are frequently employed to imply some force within an animal that causes it to behave socially. The gathering of migrating ungulates such as wildebeest (*Connochaetes taurinus*) in Africa, or swallows (*Hirundo rustica*) assembling for migration, are often attributed by the layman to their 'social instinct'. It is clearly wrong to use 'instinct' in this way and modern biologists apply the term cautiously (MANNING, 1979). To describe an event (whether gregariousness, or a new-born lamb searching for its mother's nipple) by calling it an instinct has no explanatory value at all. It simply conceals the interesting physiological, ecological and developmental questions we must ask in order to understand why animals behave as they do. *Instinctive behaviour* is a useful label for behaviour which seems inborn, being largely complete when first performed even when imitation has been denied. But, while accepting the importance of such 'inborn' skills we must not establish an artificial division between the role of the environment and that of inheritance. Social development, like anatomical development, involves close interaction between instructions from the genes and environmental conditions (Chapter 7). The relative importance of inheritance and learning varies between species: many insects live such short lives that there is little time for learning or for modifying inherited behavioural instructions.

1.2   How is social behaviour studied?

Anthropomorphism   As social animals we regularly describe and comment on the behaviour of our own and other species. In everyday conversation it is unnecessary to describe in minute details what animals do, or to offer anything but a brief explanation of their behaviour. All too often, and without being aware of it, we project our own feelings and experiences onto other species. We forget that many animals are nocturnal and quickly accuse them of being lazy or lethargic; we ask whether animals are bored or happy without questioning the relevance of these notions; and we ignore the fact that many animals emphasize quite different senses from ourselves. As scientists we must try to remain objective and avoid anthropomorphism (assigning human attributes to animals). Animal social behaviour is studied by scientists from a variety of disciplines: ecology, psychology, physiology, zoology and even anthropology. Since their interests differ each discipline contributes its own philosophy, methods and expertise. Each approach has advantages, a fact recognized by many students of behaviour who choose whatever methods are appropriate to the question being investigated.

Population biology method   Investigating ecological aspects of social behaviour may demand the methods used by population biologists. It may be necessary to sample the population to discover its density; to classify individuals according age, sex and reproductive condition and to describe how behaviour is distributed across the day and seasons. To discern whether animals have territories or non-exclusive home-ranges (p. 27) it is important to record where they go and to study interactions between neighbours.

Ethological methods Questions about social interaction and communication may require the ethological methods devised by zoologists. The animals should be watched carefully and at first preferably in a natural or semi-natural state and with a minimum of disturbance. Only later, once a good descriptive foundation has been laid, should experiments be introduced to solve particular problems. It is important to keep a clear record of what the animals do. This must be done while observing and with an open mind, since seemingly trivial acts may later turn out to be important. With experience, the animal's movements can be classified and broken down into their elements or *behaviour patterns*. Initially these are given descriptive names (e.g. wing-raising, tail-beating) and not names implying function (e.g. appeasement expression, dominance behaviour). Investigation may show that some patterns are social signals (see Chapter 5). Even then, functional names should be used with caution since the same pattern may occur in quite different contexts (p. 42), or have contrasting meanings in different species. An example of a mixture of descriptive and functional labels is given in Fig. 1–1. Although now more widely used, the ethological method was initially used by zoologist who emphasized the apparently instinctive nature of much behaviour, and paid particular attention to *fixed-action patterns* – behaviour patterns which are shown by all members of a species and are particularly resistant to modification by experience.

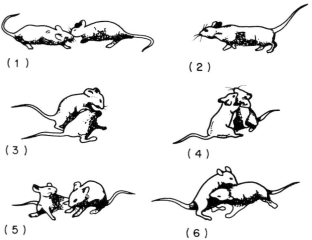

Fig. 1–1 Social behaviour patterns in the laboratory mouse (*Mus musculus*). (1) Left, nose; right, nose. (2) Stretched attention posture. (3) Left, attack. (4) Left, offensive upright posture; right, defensive upright posture. (5) Left, defensive sideways posture; right, offensive sideways posture. (6) Left, offensive upright posture; right, offensive sideways posture. (After GRANT, E. C. and MACKINTOSH, J. H. (1963). *Behaviour*, **21**, 246–59.)

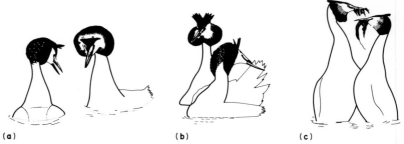

(a)   (b)   (c)

Fig. 1–2 Mutual water-courtship display of the great-crested grebe (*Podiceps cristatus*). Only three phases of the complex display are shown. (a) Each bird performs low head-waggles from side to side. (b) Bird on right shows habit-preening – a ritualized, incomplete preening movement. (c) Having dived for weed the birds have swum towards each other and risen vertically in the weed dance. (After CRAMP, S. and SIMMONS, K. E. L. (Eds) (1977). *The Birds of the Western Palearctic*, Vol. 1. Oxford University Press, Oxford.)

Most behaviour patterns do not appear in isolation, but are grouped into combinations or sequences, as in nest-building, threatening and courting. Combinations which have a communicative function are called *displays* (Fig. 1–2). A list of behaviour patterns is known as an *ethogram*.

Once he has acquired a precise language for describing an animal's behaviour the observer can proceed with his study. He can now be more selective, recording (probably on a check-sheet or a pen-recorder) only the behaviour relevant to his research question. It is a good policy to write down the research question clearly, followed by a list of the data required and an outline of how it will be analysed. If this is done there is less chance of collecting data that cannot be analysed! Most problems require the *recognition* of individual animals (either by natural or artificial markings) and *sampling* to discover the frequency and duration of behaviour (§ 6.2). For example, a study of grooming in monkeys might involve a description of the movements used in grooming and how they develop in young animals; recording the identity of animals which give and receive grooming; and recording the frequency of grooming and the total time spent in the activity. The zoologist will have, at least in the back of his mind, the question of evolution and the adaptive significance of behaviour. It is consequently important for him to have a wide appreciation of the animal's biology, including its ecology and physiology, and to compare frequently the behaviour of closely related species. Anyone attempting this kind of work is urged to read *Hints for research in animal sociology* (Chapter 9 in TINBERGEN, 1964).

Animal psychology methods Animal psychologists have played a major role in developing laboratory techniques for the study of animal behaviour. They emphasize the importance of systematically varying the animal's environment, previous experience and physiological state, in order to isolate the factors influencing its behaviour. (For details of the methods used see JEEVES, 1974.) Animal psychology is largely concerned with the problems of perception, learning, memory and motivation. Psychologists have concentrated on isolated individuals of relatively few species and have often ignored the animal's biology. Nevertheless, psychologists were historically in a good position to show the ethologist the importance of learning in social development and for devising experimental methods for studying social behaviour.

Laboratory studies   The laboratory offers close control over the animal subjects. Social interactions can be staged and experiments mechanized. Nocturnal animals can be kept on a reverse light cycle, so that they are active during our day, and then watched under red or dim light. By careful rearing in cages, age, weight, genetics, diet and previous social experience are under the experimenter's direct control. For example, the way mice retrieve young when their nest is disturbed could be compared in females who have had none, one or several litters. Detailed investigations of this sort are often only possible in the laboratory. A further advantage of the laboratory is that it permits the recording and manipulation of an animal's physiology. Physiologists are developing an understanding of the nervous and hormonal control of behaviour (MESSENGER, 1979). By means of castration, replacement therapy and assaying the level of circulating homones, it is possible to study the role of hormones in sexual behaviour, fighting or nest-building (see SLATER, 1978). Other techniques involve recording electrical activity in the brain during social behaviour or attempting to produce behaviour patterns by stimulating electrodes implanted into the brain.

Laboratory work does have its problems. Some animals are too large or too difficult to keep in captivity and it is easy for observations to become detached and the natural relevance of the behaviour forgotten. It should also be remembered that an animal's behaviour in captivity can be abnormal. In zoos, safari parks and laboratories animals may be found living alone or in unnatural social groups and suffering from environmental and social deprivation. Anyone keeping animals in captivity has a responsibility to avoid physical and psychological suffering and endangering rare species.

Field studies   Ethologists and ecologists emphasize the importance of field work for revealing the natural behaviour of animals and its adaptive significance. An outdoor life has many charms, but animals and their observers must work at all times and in all weathers. Field work has other problems. The animals being studied may be shy, hidden in cover, difficult to recognize as individuals and will usually have an unknown history. The field worker has to take what nature offers; only occasionally are carefully controlled experiments possible.

Numerical work   In both laboratory and field sufficient animals must be observed to illustrate natural variability and in order to understand individual idiosyncrasies. Modern trends in social behaviour studies include paying more rigorous attention to hypothesis testing, methodology, quantifying behaviour, and using statistics to assess the variability between individuals or an animal's performance under different conditions. Remember, however, that excessive quantification and indiscriminate use of statistics are pointless. No amount of fancy numerical work can replace a solid knowledge of your animal or compensate for a bad choice of methods.

1.3 Why study social behaviour?

Social behaviour as an adaptation   One answer to this question would be 'because social behaviour is interesting and challenging'. This is fine, but frequently the scientist's interest is more specific. Animals behave because it is adaptive for them to do so and it is important for biologists to understand the nature of behavioural adaptations. Just as it may be adaptive for animals to have a gut for digestion, or blood that releases oxygen to the tissues under certain conditions, so it is adaptive for them to have organized movements and responses to diverse stimuli. An animal's behaviour is a vital part of its adaptation and obviously works in association with physiological and anatomical adaptations. Both non-social behaviour (such as responding to food or predators) and social behaviour (such as courting and fighting) are involved.

For example, as will be shown later, by living in a social group many animals can exist where solitary individuals would perish or would be less successful in their reproduction. Life in a group may give protection since many pairs of eyes are better than one and warning signals can be used to tell of danger. Thus common baboons (*Papio cynocephalus*) live in large groups on the open savanna; lone individuals or those in smaller groups are more susceptible to predation. Many animals can only manage to rear young by cooperating with their mates and hence we see the evolution of the pair-bond (see p. 81). The value of cooperation is also seen in termites where in the more advanced species, millions of workers contribute to the building of huge nests and tunnels. The design of these ensures that they are air-conditioned with optimal conditions (temperature, humidity and oxygen) being maintained for rearing the brood and growing the fungus on which the termites feed.

The potential flexibility of behaviour makes it an exciting adaptation. Admittedly, instinctive behaviour seems inflexible and has in fact been shaped during evolution to be so. On the other hand, much behaviour involves learning with experience. This permits a close match between individual behaviour and the environment, an important feature in the face of environmental variability. In long-lived animals, learning allows information which is not coded in the genes to be passed from generation to generation. The capacity to learn must of course be inherited.

Social behaviour and the physiologist   There is a close relationship between an animal's physiology and behaviour. Assessing physiological activity involves not only the traditional physiological measures (e.g. water balance, level of blood sugar) but also, in appropriate cases, measuring behavioural responses and social interaction. For example, to understand the role of homones in bird reproduction a physiologist might study their production and their effect on the reproductive tract and on sexual behaviour, nest-building, maternal behaviour and aggression.

Comparative studies of animals and man   In many situations it is wrong to experiment with people, and other species take our place in the apparatus. Such experiments accept that man is an animal sharing many anatomical, physiological and behavioural features with other species. Generalizations from one species to another always require caution, especially since we know that closely related species (and even separate populations of the same species) can differ considerably in their social behaviour. Each species has evolved in its own environment and superficial similarities may conceal subtle but significant differences. It has recently been popular to emphasize 'man the animal' but let us not underestimate the importance of man's language, foresight and culture. Remember also that the societies of animals and men are so variable that it is possible to find 'evidence' supporting almost any theory of human behaviour. Animal models of human behaviour are sometimes completely unnecessary and man's social behaviour can be studied directly. There are disciplines devoted to this end including sociology, social anthropology and psychology.

Some anthropologists have turned their attention to the social behaviour of wild primates in an attempt to make predictions about the social life of early man. They argue that if particular patterns of social organization are characteristic of particular environments, one might, knowing the environment of early man, be able to predict his social organization. This is unfortunately, a simplification. On the other hand, studies of animal social behaviour elucidate principles applicable to man, help us formulate hypotheses about our own behaviour and develop methods applicable to studies of human social behaviour. For example, ethological studies of people emphasize the importance of subtle gestures used in human greetings and other face to face communication.

Animal welfare   One direct application of social behaviour studies is found in agriculture. Modern intensive rearing methods for cattle, pigs and chickens involve quite unnatural conditions. Scientists are called upon to investigate behaviour problems and the effects they have on productivity and health (see ARCHER, 1979).

2 Natural Selection and Social Behaviour

2.1 Natural selection

Adaptation to the environment   An *adaptation* is a feature with the function of aiding the survival and reproduction of an organism and an animal's behaviour is a vital part of its adaptation to the environment. Before examining the adaptive significance of social behaviour we must pause to look at the whole phenomenon of natural selection. The modern synthesis of the theory of natural selection is based on the ideas of Darwin and Wallace but modified to take account of the laws of inheritance as we now know them (see EDWARDS, 1977; SMITH, 1975).

Ignoring short-term fluctuations, the number of individuals in a species remains roughly constant in spite of an organism's theoretical capacity to replace itself many times over (see SOLOMON, 1976). In practice, most descendants do not survive: a high death rate is common. Some mortality is random, but it is the non-random mortality which is of prime importance in evolution. Individuals are variable and differ in many ways. Consequently, some are less well adapted to their environment and tend to die before reproduction or do not reproduce as efficiently as others. Relatively poorly adapted individuals therefore contribute fewer young to future generations. As offspring inherit genes from their parents, the genes from the better adapted animals increase in relative frequency and future generations are on average better adapted to their environment. This evolutionary process of *natural selection* never ceases; environments change and consequently so does the adaptiveness of characters. A vital part of this argument is that the characters inherited from parents are those coded in their genes. Characters acquired during the parents' life are not passed to the offspring in the gametes. In higher animals, behaviour may be passed on by learning; this is the process of *cultural transmission*.

Another important distinction is between *genotype* and *phenotype*. An organism's genetic constitution is its genotype. During development the genotype interacts with the environment to produce the phenotype – the organism itself with all its observable characteristics. Natural selection acts on the phenotype but only features coded in the genotype can be inherited.

An animal's adaptation is influenced by all aspects of its biology. Our task is to examine adaptations involving social behaviour, but we must not be too blinkered. Natural selection acts on anatomical, physiological and behavioural features which are interdependent in the whole organism, and selection takes place at all stages of the life cycle. For example, most sperm never fertilize an ovum; many organisms die while immature; some reproduce but are inadequate parents. Clearly, selection before and during reproduction is most important. In a few species, like our own, where post-reproductive individuals are valuable sources of cultural information for their offspring, natural selection may act post-reproductively.

Genetic fitness   The relative adequacy of an individual's adaptation is measured by its *genetic fitness*, which is defined as the contribution of its genes to the next generation relative to the contribution of other individuals in the population. This is usually estimated by the number of offspring reared. (Note that early biologists defined fitness differently – in terms of health, stature and vigour.) Since only animals which survive to maturity can reproduce, one can expect behaviour that aids survival to be perpetuated in offspring and hence to evolve. Similarly, behaviour that increases reproductive efficiency will evolve. Examination of much social behaviour shows that it increases fitness by promoting the survival of the individual and its offspring. For example, the close cooperation between male and female European robins (*Erithacus rubecula*) during setting up a territory, brooding, warning of danger and rearing young has evolved because individuals who were inadequate at these activities (or who chose inadequate mates) were less successful. Figure 2–1 records how cooperation between a breeding pair of kittiwake gulls broke down and their brood was lost.

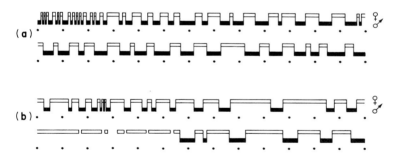

Fig. 2–1   The role of male and female kittiwakes in the incubation pattern of a successful (**a**) and unsuccessful (**b**) pair. The record for each pair (which should be read from left to right) has been cut into two to fit it on the page. The horizontal line (open for the female, solid for the male) shows when the birds were incubating. Vertical lines show change-overs between male and female. The dots indicate midnight and the distance between adjacent dots denotes 24 h. The successful pair soon established a clear rhythm but in the unsuccessful pair the male did not play an equal part. When he stayed away the female incubated for 48 h but was eventually forced to leave the nest. The eggs presumably chilled and the embryos died. (After COULSON, J. C. (1972). *Proc. 15th Int. Ornithological Cong.*, 424–33.)

2.2   The inheritance of behaviour

Genes controlling behaviour   The inheritance of genes controlling behaviour is essential if behaviour is to evolve. Even in cases of cultural transmission animals must inherit the ability to learn and use the behaviour to which they are exposed. To elucidate the genetic mechanisms involved in the inheritance of behaviour several different types of experiments have been done. These can be only briefly discussed here; for a more detailed review see MANNING (1979). Since the development of the behavioural phenotype is so dependent on the interaction between inheritance and experience (p, 67), the environment must be carefully controlled during these experiments. Only in this way will repeatable and interpretable results be obtained. One method for overcoming this problem is to work with fixed-action patterns, the development of which is relatively unaffected by experience. Two examples follow.

Some strains of honeybees (*Apis mellifera*) are more resistant to bacterial infection because the workers uncap brood cells and remove dead larvae. By a series of breeding experiments, in which inbred queens were crossed with drones by means of artificial insemination, it was discovered that uncapping and removing dead larvae are controlled by two separate recessive genes. It is possible, for example, to breed bees which uncap cells containing dead larvae but do not remove the corpses. Male fruit flies (*Drosophila melanogaster*) carrying the mutant gene *yellow*, which affects body pigmentation, have reduced mating success when paired with wild-type (i.e. non-mutant) females. It is not their colour that reduces their success but their courtship behaviour which includes relatively less wing-vibration, an important signal to the female (Fig. 5–1). The gene *yellow* therefore reduces a male's fitness and, in the wild, males carrying the gene would be rapidly selected against.

Selection experiments   Selection experiments must also be considered since they demonstrate the genetic variability affecting behaviour which is available for selection in natural populations. This is demonstrated by the effect of artificial selection on fruit fly mating speed, i.e. the duration of courtship. Two experimental groups each of 50 virgin pairs were removed from the parent stock of *D. melanogaster* and from each group a fast and slow mating line was selected as follows. The 50 pairs were mixed in a chamber and the first 10 pairs to mate were sucked out for breeding a fast line and the last 10 pairs similarly selected for a slow line. In subsequent generations fast and slow maters were selected as appropriate. To show that mating speed did not change without selection, control matings were timed at intervals using flies from the parent stock. The fast and slow lines diverged by the second generation and remained distinct. In this case we are not seeing the effect of a single gene but the accumulation in the flies of the small effects of genes at many loci. By means of similar selection experiments it has proved possible to select successfully for numerous traits in various animals. For example, rats have been produced which are 'bright' or 'dull', 'emotional' or 'non-emotional'.

Artificial selection experiments usually involve selecting one character, but it must not be forgotten that in nature selection acts on the whole phenotype. There is always a compromise between perfecting a single character and the effect of this on an animal's total adaptation. Brightly coloured plumage may play an important role in courtship but an ornate bird may be more noticeable to predators. Some birds such as chaffinches (*Fringilla coelebs*) and mallards (*Anas platyrhynchos*) are dimorphic (the male and female being coloured differently), suggesting that the optimum colouration differs with the contrasting roles of the sexes. Advantages and disadvantages are balanced; the product of selection is a compromise.

2.3   Individual selection

Selection involves differential survival and reproduction and can operate at various levels. In this discussion so far, the process by which characters become established because of their effect on the survival and reproduction of the individual has been emphasized. This is termed *individual selection*. For example, individuals will be selected against if they are relatively slow at escaping from predators, relatively poor at caring for their young or inadequate at courting.

Sexual selection   A special category of individual selection, of particular interest to students of social behaviour, is *sexual selection* which results from the different abilities of individuals to effect matings and the differences in quality of the mates acquired. Consider the position of a female ready to mate. To produce the best possible offspring and so maximize her genetic contribution to the next generation, she must choose the best male available. For example, only male red grouse (*Lagopus lagopus*) with territories are chosen as mates and in species where males gather on communal mating grounds or leks (e.g. black grouse *Lyrurus tetrix* and wild turkeys *Meleagris gallopavo*, Fig. 3–3), the subordinate males obtain few copulations (p. 24). Some components of courtship displays and special morphological adaptations, such as bright plumages, are apparently used by males to attract females and by females to choose between males. There must be a positive correlation between a male's fitness and his looks, displays and his ability to successfully compete against other males in, for example, gaining a territory (see Chapter 8). Sexual selection which results from the differential choice by members of one sex for the other is called *intersexual selection* or *epigamic selection*.

Another characteristic of reproductive behaviour is that members of one sex (usually male) often compete amongst each other for access to the other sex. Competition may be for mates directly or for a resource such as a territory which subsequently plays a major role in obtaining a mate and reproduction. Male red grouse compete for territories; those without them do not gain mates and usually die before the breeding season starts. During the rut (mating season), male red deer (*Cervus elaphus*) fight each other for possession of a group of females and hence the chance to mate with them (Fig. 2–2). Sexual selection which results from this type of competition between members of one sex is called *intrasexual selection*. Males who compete successfully against other males obtain more females and will pass more genes to the next generation. This has led to the evolution of the fighting skills and anatomical features used in intrasexual strife or intimidation, for instance red deer antlers and the huge bulk of male Northern elephant seals (*Mirounga angustirostris*). Sexual selection will operate whenever there is a competititve mating situation. It will be most extreme in *polygamous* animals (i.e. where an individual has two or more mates who are not also mated to others) or *promiscuous* animals (i.e. where there are no bonds between partners, each animal mating with several partners).

Note carefully that in all these cases (and in the other evolutionary arguments presented) conscious reasoning by the animals is not implied. It is not necessary to assert that an animal thinks, for example, 'I must choose the best male here to ensure that my children are strong and can carry my genes to the next generation'. Animals are genetically programmed to act in these ways because their ancestors which showed the behaviour were more successful than those that did not. The genes controlling the behaviour were consequently passed to future generations.

Fig. 2–2   Fighting red deer stags. (From TINBERGEN, 1964.)

2.4 Kin selection

2.4.1 Altruism and inclusive fitness

One result of individual selection has been the evolution of *parental care*. The energy that parents expend while rearing their young is enormous; its adaptive significance immense. There are endless examples. Consider a pair of great tits (*Parus major*) who together make 300–400 nest visits each day carrying food, or the female common baboon who is rarely out of contact with her infant for its first two months of life, carries it until it is seven and a half months old and protects it through five or more years of immaturity. Attention has been focused recently on the activities related to parental care in which animals give aid to others who are *not* their own offspring. Honeybee workers, for instance, spend their lives caring for their mother, sisters and brothers; many animals give calls which warn others of approaching danger; and adolescent female monkeys of many species carry and care for their younger siblings. These are fascinating instances of social behaviour. In each case animals act *altruistically* by risking themselves for others, or by expending energy they could have put into their own reproduction. How could such behaviour evolve? One answer is that animals behave altruistically towards their kin (e.g. brothers, cousins) with whom they share some genes. The net result of an altruistic act is, therefore, to increase the relative frequency in the population of the recipient's genes *including those shared*: the altruist's *inclusive fitness* has been increased. In this way selection has favoured animals helping close kin, so long as the benefits (in terms of shared genes perpetuated) outweighs any direct loss of fitness (e.g. loss of energy or life by the altruist). It follows that animals which helped unrelated strangers would be selected against since they would perpetuate the strangers' genes in competition to their own.

This process, which leads to an altrusitic act being established because of its effects on the survival and reproduction of the possessor's relatives, is called *kin selection*. Note that the arguments used are a direct extension of those used to show the adaptiveness of parental care. The terms 'individual selection' and 'kin selection' are therefore not mutually exclusive. Imagine there were two kin groups (social groups composed of kin, e.g. bee colonies) or kin networks (a network of related individuals in a large social unit, such as a baboon group) and that only one had evolved an altruistic trait. All other things being equal we would expect the altruists to have a higher survival rate and to produce more young and so eventually to replace the non-altruists. Kin selection therefore involves differential survival and reproduction of groups of related animals.

2.4.2 Kin selection in Hymenoptera

The evolution of altruism by kin selection can be illustrated by examining in some detail an intriguing problem posed by the social insects. How have the sterile workers evolved in the Hymenoptera (bees, wasps and ants) when their sterility prevents them from contributing offspring to the next generation? Details of honeybee colonies are given in Chapter 4, but at this point the genetic relationship between members of a colony and the method of sex determination must be appreciated. Although the honeybee is used as an example the same principles apply to other social Hymenoptera.

The *queen* is a fertile female and is diploid (i.e. carrying the usual two sets of chromosomes). She stores sperm received on her mating flight and can control whether or not her eggs are fertilized. Fertilized eggs are diploid and develop into females, most of which are sterile *workers*, but with a special diet they can develop into new queens. Unfertilized eggs are haploid (i.e. they have only one set of chromosomes, receiving none from the male) and develop into males called *drones*. In honeybees (and other Hymenoptera) there is therefore a *haplo-diploid* system, which is unusual: humans are, of course, *diplo-diploid*.

The haplo-diploid system offers the key to Hymenopteran altruism. Each daughter bee receives half of her genes from her mother (queen) and half from her father (drone). When a queen fertilizes one of her own gametes with stored sperm, each daughter receives the *same* genes from the drone since haploid males can produce only one type of gamete. The queen, being diploid, produces gametes which are not identical since there is a random reassortment of homologous chromosomes during the meiotic reduction division (Fig. 2–3a). As the figure shows, the daughters share *on average* half of the genes received from their mother. Since they get only half of their total genes from their mother this shared proportion represents a quarter (0.25) of their genotype. When genes received from queen and drone are considered together we see that sisters have on average three-quarters (0.75) of their genes in common by descent: 0.5 (from the drone) + 0.25 (from the queen) (Fig. 2–3b). Sisters are therefore more closely related than mothers are to sons or daughters (0.5). By helping their mother (the queen) to reproduce and eventually to produce new queens (sisters of the workers), the workers have more in common with the next generation (0.75) than if they had themselves reproduced (0.5). This example illustrates the logical reasoning used in this type of analysis which goes some way towards explaining the evolution of hymenopteran worker altruism. Inevitably, there are some complicating factors which cannot be discussed here. All the figures given above assume there is no inbreeding (e.g. brother–sister mating); this would increase the relationship between individuals.

2.4.3   *Kin selection in diplo-diploid organisms*

The same type of reasoning can be used to explain the evolution of altruism in termites (Isoptera) or other animals in which both sexes are diploid. A person will have half of his mother's genes and half of his

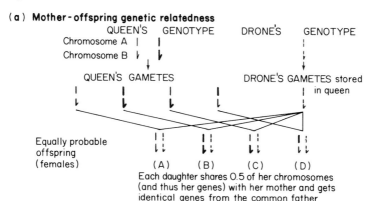

(a) Mother-offspring genetic relatedness

QUEEN'S   GENOTYPE   DRONE'S   GENOTYPE
Chromosome A
Chromosome B

QUEEN'S GAMETES   DRONE'S GAMETES stored
                                                    in queen

Equally probable
offspring
(females)   (A)   (B)   (C)   (D)

Each daughter shares 0.5 of her chromosomes
(and thus her genes) with her mother and gets
identical genes from the common father

(b) Sister-sister genetic relatedness

Pick any daughter genotype and compare it with the
possible genotypes of her sisters

For example:

| | | Genetic similarity based on proportion of chromosomes and hence genes from: | | |
		QUEEN	DRONE	TOTAL SIMILARITY
(C)	(A)	0.25	0.5	0.75
	(B)	0.25	0.5	0.75
	(C)	0.5	0.5	1.00
	(D)	0	0.5	0.5
Average proportion of genes shared between sisters		0.25 +	0.5 =	0.75

Fig. 2-3 (a) Degree of genetic relationship of a queen honeybee and her female offspring, the workers. (b) The genetic relationship of the workers (sisters). For the sake of simplicity, only two chromosomes are considered. Sisters are more closely related to one another (average = 0.75) than they would be to their own progeny (0.5). (Redrawn after ALCOCK, J. (1979). *Animal Behaviour an Evolutionary Approach.* 2nd ed. Sinauer Associates, Sunderland, Mass.)

father's, and on average he will share half of his genes with his siblings. In genetic terms it is therefore only worth him risking his life if in doing so he is going to save more than two of his children or more than two full siblings or more than eight first cousins and so on. Help by one animal to another will be selected when the ratio of the gain of fitness to the recipient, to the loss of fitness of the altruist, is greater than the reciprocal of the relatedness between the animals. It is important to express the principle in this general way since in many instances the help given by one animal to another does not involve sterility or a high risk of dying.

When discussing man arguments must not be taken too far, since *cultural* factors are of prime importance in determining behaviour: cultural pressures lead people to behave as society expects them to behave, a feature called *role playing* by sociologists. It must also be noted that animals can gain additional benefits from helping others: adolescent female monkeys who help mothers look after infants learn the behaviour involved and are therefore more competent when their own babies are born. For more information on kin selection see SMITH (1975) and BROWN (1975).

2.5 Population selection*

Another possible level of selection is that between populations, in which some populations expand and divide, while less well-adapted populations die out. *Population selection* should be contrasted with individual selection, but the position with reference to kin selection is less clear since under some circumstances a small population could be a network of related animals.

2.5.1 Does population selection occur in nature?

An example will perhaps clarify the idea of population selection. Imagine (*hypothetical* statement (*a*)) that there are two populations of birds, one of which is composed of individuals that limit their breeding to suit the food supplies predicted to be available in the next winter and so keep down population mortality, and a second population which does not do this. Would the first population, with the ability to limit breeding, be at a selective advantage? Would it expand and split giving rise to similar populations while populations of the second type became extinct? Presented in this way it appears that 'yes' is the obvious answer to these questions; we shall presently see that the answer is probably 'no'. We are now touching on a stimulating controversy which clearly demonstrates the interdependence between the study of social behaviour, population regulation and evolution. The most publicized protagonist of population selection has been V. C. Wynne-Edwards; his antagonists are too numerous to mention.

Let us look at some more *hypothetical* statements. It is frequently stated (*b*) that many animals control their fighting so as not to injure or kill members of their own species, (*c*) that animals which migrate in times of

* Synonyms for population selection include group selection and interdemic selection. Note that some biologists (e.g. WILSON, 1975) use group selection in a more general and highly misleading way to include both kin selection and population selection.

hardship do so to give those remaining a greater chance of survival, and (d) that animals place themselves at risk to warn other animals of approaching danger. These four statements (a–d) suggest that animals may act in an altruistic way *beneficial to the population* (or species) but somewhat *disadvantageous to themselves*. Such cases (referred to as *group-related adaptations*) must be examined carefully. Two lines of reasoning are available. First, each case can be argued in a theoretical manner constructing hypotheses and predicting their effects. This approach demonstrates that individual selection would make group-related adaptations unstable. If in situation (a) non-altruist 'selfish' animals arose who did not limit their reproduction they would increase at the expense of the others. Individual selection would ensure that the genes for selfishness increased relative to those for the group-related adaptation. Note that this reasoning does not exclude the evolution of an optimum clutch size, since even the most selfish individuals will be at a disadvantage if they regularly attempt to produce more young than they can satisfactorily rear. For population selection to be possible *all* individuals in a population would have to have the altruistic trait from the start, and non-altruistic mutations and immigration of non-altruistic animals would not have to occur.

A second approach involves examining what actually happens in nature. Long-term studies of bird populations show that brood size is close to the average number the parents can rear and that high mortality has the effect of keeping the population size down. There is little indication that birds keep their brood sizes artificially low as statement (a) would require. In this way, most so-called group-related adaptations can be more simply explained. The phenomenon either does not exist, as in (a), or can be explained on the basis of kin selection (d) and individual selection (b and c). Migration in time of hardship will, for example, be associated with a certain probability of survival for the migrant. If migration increases fitness, then it will be selected for on the basis of individual selection.

2.5.2 Conclusion

In practice, theoretical evolutionary arguments are never as neat as implied here. All hypotheses involve assumptions whose significance is debatable and so the population selection versus individual selection controversy is perpetuated. Mathematical models demonstrate that population selection is possible but improbable under most circumstances. Logically, individual selection is more powerful because it involves fewer and simpler assumptions which are more frequently encountered in nature. The present evidence therefore indicates that population selection would be unstable and of little importance relative to individual selection (see SMITH, 1975).

With this evolutionary background we can now probe more deeply and directly into the study of social behaviour, starting with animal groups.

3 Animal Groups

3.1 The diversity of animal groups

Animals often do not live alone: red deer live in herds, wolves (*Canis lupus*) in packs, fish in schools, monkeys in troops, mute swans (*Cygnus olor*) in pairs . . . and so on. Closer examination reveals a bewildering variety of animal groups. One way to aid our understanding is to classify groups on the basis of certain key characteristics, but although classification is helpful, we must not draw too rigid a distinction between categories. The differences between the group types defined here are one of degree; no firm boundaries exist. All animal groups are dynamic having an important capacity for change. Indeed many animals are *solitary* for some or most of their lives, a feature considered in Chapter 4.

Societies Animal groups which conform to all or most of the following characteristics are called *societies* (examined further in § 3.2).

(*a*) Membership is limited to animals of one species and to a particular set of individuals. The group's integrity may be based on a group odour, as in honeybees, or individual recognition, as in birds and mammals.

(*b*) A definite attraction exists between members, they may disperse for some activities but they eventually reassemble. Animals meeting for a brief encounter (e.g. two fruit flies courting and mating) are not considered to be a society; a longer association is required.

(*c*) Members communicate with each other. They do so more frequently, and using different social signals, than they do with members of other societies.

(*d*) There is a high degree of cooperation between members. Division of labour is frequent, some individuals specializing in one task, others in another. In small societies (such as wolf packs and pairs of nesting birds) individual recognition is an important basis for cooperation. In large societies (such as ant and termite colonies) individual recognition is not feasible. Cooperation is then based on caste (see p. 27) recognition and the ability to distinguish between animals participating in different activities.

(*e*) The activity of members is frequently sychronized, especially for feeding, resting, moving and mating.

Anonymous groups Another type of animal group is the *anonymous group*. Typical examples are the large herds of migrating wildebeest in Africa and caribou (*Rangifer tarandus*) in the tundra, fish schools, roosting flocks of starlings and the migratory flocks of many birds. Anonymous groups do not share all the characteristics just noted for societies. Movements may be carefully coordinated but otherwise there is little cooperation and division of labour. Some anonymous groups (e.g. non-breeding flocks of greylag geese, *Anser anser*) are composed of families but they still have a more open membership, not being restricted to specific sets of individuals. These features are important since much social behaviour within a society is determined by the individual identity of the interacting animals. In anonymous groups different classes of individuals may be recognizable, for instance young or very subordinate animals. But with individual recognition limited (usually by the large numbers present), social hierarchies are rare and leadership and other division of labour poorly established. Most anonymous groups are composed of a single species but multi-species flocks of birds (e.g. finches) and groups of monkeys do occur and it is of considerable interest to know why.

Aggregations   There is another type of animal grouping which largely forms because of the common attraction of individuals to a resource or stimulus. Such groups are called *aggregations* and they include fruit flies around rotting fruit, moths around a lamp at night, butterflies collecting on their food plants, and woodlice collecting in humid places under stones. Aggregations share few of the characteristics noted for societies; there is virtually no internal organization of the group.

3.2   Different types of societies

An animal's social partners, social behaviour and opportunity for learning from other animals are limited by the type of society in which it lives. For example, young game birds and many ducks are reared by their mothers without the assistance of their father. Consequently they have little early interaction with mature males. Similarly, young animals such as gibbons or song birds which are reared in their parents' territory, have social interactions with other young limited to their siblings. Only later do they interact with young from other families. In some monkeys (such as the patas monkey (*Erythrocebus patas*) – a swiftly running, cryptic creature of the African savannas) most males live without females in bachelor groups and have little opportunity to behave heterosexually. For many animals the society is therefore the *social environment*, part of the background against which all social behaviour must be examined and assessed.

Societies are far from uniform: they vary markedly in different types of animals. Some species even have more than one type of society at a time or different societies depending on the season or location. The patas monkey, for example, always has harem groups consisting of a single male with several females and young, and groups of bachelor males. Outside the rut, red deer separate into bachelor groups and groups of females with their young. Chaffinches live in family units during the breeding season but in loose flocks at other times. The causes of this variable division of populations into societies are extremely interesting,

Table 1   Examples of different types of societies

Type of society	Examples
One-parent family	Polar bear (*Thalarctos maritimus*), black bear (*Ursus arctos*), hedgehog (*Erinaceus europaeus*), mallard duck, black grouse, stickleback fish, many rodents
Family	Song birds, mute swan, golden jackal (*Canis aureus*)
Extended one-parent family	Honeybee, wasp (*Vespula vulgaris*), ants
Extended family	Termites, wolf, white-handed gibbon (*Hylobates lar*)
Harem	Wild horse (*Equus caballus*), zebra (*Equus burchelli*), vicuna (*Vicugna vicugna*), red deer, gelada baboon (*Theropithecus gelada*), patas monkey, sea lions (*Otaria*)
Female groups	African elephants (*Loxodonta africana*), wild pigs (*Sus scrofa*), red deer
Bachelor groups	See text
Multi-male groups	Common baboon, rhesus monkey, spotted hyaena (*Crocuta crocuta*), African hunting dogs (*Lycaon pictus*), African lion (*Panthera leo*)

and will be looked at in Chapter 8. By way of preparation, we must now examine the characteristics of different types of societies (Table 1).

One-parent family   The simplest society is the *one-parent family* in which the adults mate, but only one parent, usually the female, stays to rear the young. In sticklebacks (*Gasterosteus aculeatus*) this is done by the male.

Family   Many animals live in *families* in which both parents rear the young. The parents may or may not mate for life and the young leave the parents before any subsequent broods are produced. In some birds, such as black-headed gulls (*Larus ridibundus*) and herring gulls (*L. argentatus*), numerous mated pairs gather into colonies to reproduce. Each pair has a nest site and a small territory on which to rear its young. The families are not completely independent, each gaining protection from living in the colony. Frequently the same birds return year after year, often with the same mate. Non-reproductive individuals, usually immatures, show less rigid attachment and come and go throughout the reproductive season.

Extended family   In *extended families* (involving one or both parents) there is an overlap of broods and the young may help to rear their siblings. These are particularly interesting societies because they involve altruistic behaviour including, in some cases, a suppression of reproduction in the mature young.

Harem   In some mammals an adult reproductive male has a *harem* of several females and their young. These may be permanent, as in zebras, vicunas (a South American relative of the camel), patas monkeys and gelada baboons (a primate of the high Ethiopean mountains), or restricted to the breeding season, as in red deer and sea lions.

Female group   When harems occur only seasonally for mating purposes as in the red deer, the females may live at other times of the year in *female groups*. These are composed of females and their young, unaccompanied by adult males (Fig. 3–1). Maturing males are eventually excluded from harems and female groups and as a consequence most adult males at any one time have no access to mature females. They live solitarily or in all-male societies called *bachelor groups* (or all-male groups). These are less stable than harems or female groups. Periodically a harem owner is ousted and replaced by a male from a bachelor group.

Multi-male group   Some of the most familiar primates and some carnivores live in *multi-male groups* comprising several adult reproductive males with several adult reproductive females and their young. In rhesus macaque monkeys (*Macaca mulatta*) and common baboons the adolescent males often move to a new group, a behaviour which reduces inbreeding. The promiscuous mating in these societies has some interesting consequences, as explained in the next section.

Fig. 3–1   Two matrilineal family groups of African elephants. (From DOUGLAS-HAMILTON, I. and O. (1975). *Among the Elephants*. Collins and Harvill Press, London.)

3.3   Kinship

The importance of kinship   In section 2.4.2 the genetic relationship between honeybees in a colony was examined and it was seen how this helped in understanding their social behaviour. Before we can suggest that altruism in other societies has evolved by kin selection we need to know that the altruist and recipient are closely related. If they are not, some other explanation is necessary. In one-parent families and female groups we know the relationship between mother and young (or the father and young in those species where the roles are reversed) but, unless we are making a careful study using marked animals, we are ignorant of the other parent's identity. In many cases a female may have more than one mate and her young may be only half-sibs.

Kinship in multi-male groups   Perhaps the greatest problems arise in multi-male groups of mammals. Here the animals are promiscuous and while a mother's identity is obvious, any of several males could be her offsprings' father. In common baboons and rhesus macaques mothers know their young (and vice versa), but as far as we can tell fathers do not know their young (and vice versa). Similarly, monkeys know their maternal sibs (i.e. siblings with the same mother) but not their paternal sibs to whom they are equally related genetically. Methodological attempts to overcome this *paternity problem* include identifying the male who copulated with a female when she was most likely to conceive and methods of paternity exclusion using blood groups or other inherited biochemical differences between individuals. This is, of course, difficult with wild animals.

The paternity problem has important consequences. First, it makes it difficult to test hypotheses on the adaptive significance of a male's behaviour, since when a male lives in a multi-male group we cannot yet determine his lifetime production of young and so measure his fitness (p. 9). Secondly, it has resulted in the *matrilineal* organization of multi-male societies. These societies are composed of genealogies traceable through the female line from mother to daughter and sons, to the daughter's daughters and sons, and so on. One study of a group of 62 rhesus macaques established that only two animals, both adult males, were born outside the group. The remaining monkeys were members of six matrilineal genealogies each of which included 5–13 animals (Fig. 3–2). These monkeys live on Cayo Santiago, an island in the Carribean, and are descendents of Indian rhesus macaques introduced in 1938. Each monkey is tattooed with a number permitting identification.

Matrilineal kinship and macaque social behaviour   Careful observation has shown that matrilineal kinship influences individual social behaviour in these multi-male primate societies. The rhesus mothers form the stable core of the group and maintain a special relationship with their offspring even into adulthood. As new siblings are born the older siblings interact less and less with their mother but develop strong relations with other close relatives. Elder sisters frequently play with and care for their younger siblings. In contrast, male offspring associate more with other males and less closely with female relatives. They eventually leave the group. Matrilineal relatives tend to sit or lie together when resting and to

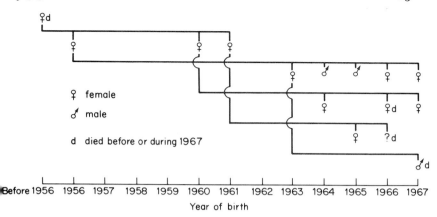

Fig. 3–2   A rhesus macaque matrilineal genealogy. (After LOY, J. (1971). *Primates*, **12** (1), 1–31.)

groom more amongst themselves than with non-relatives (see p. 65). We also know that matrilineal relatives associate closely in chimpanzees, common baboons and Japanese macaques (*Macaca fuscata*), the other species for which we have long-term data. In chimpanzees, with their more flexible societies, males often move independently of their mothers and sisters but still occasionally return to them as adults. Macaque mothers actively defend their offspring against attack, and siblings also support each other in fights. As a result, young from high-ranking mothers become high-ranking; those of low-ranking mothers, low-ranking (p. 62). The influence of matrilineal kinship manifests itself in still other ways. It seems that male macaques and chimpanzees rarely mate with their mothers. Brother rhesus macaques even aid each other when they change groups as young adults or adolescents: an elder brother who has previously changed groups, may groom and protect a young brother with the result that it is accepted by the new group. Finally, when Japanese macaque groups split into two groups they divide between matrilines.

Kinship in other mammals   We lack these intimate details for most other animals but kinship can be expected to be important whenever animals live in groups that are stable over a number of generations. Owing to the inevitably close bond between a mother mammal and her young, the predominance of matrilineal kinship will prove to be an important rule. This is known to be the case in sheep (*Ovis aries*) and African elephants. In each species, females of several generations and their young associate, and in elephants the bonds between some females may even span 50 years. By contrast the adult males remain in the social group in the cooperatively hunting African lion, spotted hyaena and African hunting dog. Again the group members seem to be closely related. In a lion group the adult females are sisters or cousins and the adult males, which will have moved into the pride from elsewhere, are also closely related.

Kinship and cooperation in birds   There is increasing information on birds in which more than one pair use a single nest or cooperatively feed and protect the young. Several detailed studies have revealed kinship between cooperating individuals. In the Tasmanian native hen (*Tribonyx mortierii*) brothers may share a female, and in Australian blue wrens (*Malurus cyaneus*) sons may help to rear their parents' subsequent broods. In wild turkeys there is a remarkably persistent association of kin. Brothers from a brood form a sibling group and, as a result of fighting, a hierarchy is established first within sibling groups and secondly between them. During the mating season the brothers display in unison to attract females, but *mating* is restricted almost entirely to the highest ranking male of the highest ranking sibling group (Fig. 3–3). In one study only six males accounted for all the matings out of 170 males on the display grounds.

As we have seen, many members of a society can be closely related. It is obvious, however, that too close a genetic relationship in a society will produce inbreeding and reduced individual fitness. Two behaviours which limit inbreeding have been mentioned – reduced mating between close relatives and the exchange of animals between groups. As in other situations, natural selection presumably results in an optimum, in this case a balance between the advantages and disadvantages of the dispersal and long-term association of kin.

Fig. 3–3   Cooperative courtship in wild turkeys. Two pairs of male siblings (and a solitary male) are shown giving the stereotyped strutting display (tail fanned, wings drooping) to the female standing on the left; the movements of each pair are almost perfectly synchronized. (After WATTS, C. R. and STOKES, A. W. (1971). *The Social Order of Turkeys.* © 1971 by Scientific American, Inc. All rights reserved.)

4 Social Organization

4.1 What is social organization?

Characterizing animals by the groups in which they live is insufficient unless coupled with other aspects of their natural history. How do societies interact with each other? How do solitary animals disperse themselves over the habitat? Is social behaviour distributed in a predictable way within a society? How stable are these features, do they change with the seasons? These are some of the questions pursued here.

Definitions of social organization Individuals do not interact at random. Whatever species is examined, some regularity is found in the pattern of social relationships. This order is referred to as *social organization* but unfortunately this term has been used in several ways, each emphasizing different aspects of social behaviour. It has been used for instance: (*a*) to refer to the type or types of society typical of a particular species (e.g. a bird flock, mated pair, multi-male group); (*b*) to describe the ways in which individuals or societies are spatially and behaviourally related to each other (e.g. 'the social organization is a territorial one', 'the social organization is a dominance hierarchy'); (*c*) to emphasize that the behaviour within a society is ordered and predictable and therefore shows 'social organization', emphasis being usually placed on aggression or on the division of labour between individuals. These definitions are too narrow. Social organization is a complex phenomenon made up of a *system* of interacting components. It is best defined as *the pattern of individual relationships seen within a population at a particular time.*

The dynamic nature of social organization Social organization is not a fixed species-specific characteristic; it is a flexible pattern of individual relationships resulting from an interaction between social behaviour, the present environment and the species' past history (see Chapter 8). Because of this interaction there may be differences in social organization within a species. Reference should therefore be made to the social organization of a *population* and *not* to the social organization of a *species*. Social organization is *dynamic* rather than static. With different ecological conditions we can expect behaviour patterns to occur with different frequencies and intensities to produce a social organization that is adaptive to current circumstances.

The social organization of solitary animals When discussing social organization, attention is usually focused on animals living in societies. It is quite legitimate, however, to refer to the social organization of solitary animals when these have a distinct pattern of relationships between neighbours. In autumn, male and female European robins may be solitary within their territories but they are clearly organized with reference to their neighbours. The same applies to male warblers, newly arrived on their breeding grounds in spring. Mammals often live solitary lives or, in the case of females, live alone with their young. Examples include common shrews (*Sorex araneus*), black bears and the orang-utan (*Pongo pygmaeus*). Domestic cats often appear to be relativedly solitary creatures, but neighbouring cats are very much aware of each other.

4.2 Describing social organization

There are four main features required for the study of social organization: (a) *population demography* – the statistics of the population and of any groups in which the animals live; (b) *population dispersion and spacing behaviour* – how animals are spaced out and the behavioural mechanisms involved;.(c) *intragroup social behaviour* – the social behaviour shown between group members; (d) *changes in the above features with time*. We must also be concerned with the *variability* in these parameters across individuals, societies and populations. In the following discussion most attention will be paid to birds and mammals living in societies.

4.2.1 Population demography

It is first important to discover the kinds of individuals present, their life span, population density, reproductive rate and relative participation in reproduction. These are some of the basic parameters that ecologists measure when studying populations (SOLOMON, 1976). In a study of Barbary macaques (*Macaca sylvanus*) (Fig. 6–5) in North Africa, several months were spent studying the population before analysing the monkeys' social behaviour in detail. Every time monkeys were seen in the forest their location and subsequent movements were noted on a map. Particularly noticeable individuals were recorded to build up a list of recognizable animals and the monkeys were counted, aged and sexed. It is often impossible to count wild animals outright and repeated sample counts must be made. The presence of recognizable or marked individuals makes this much easier. (When small, cryptic mammals such as mice and voles are studied direct observation may be impossible: other methods must be relied upon such as capturing the animals, marking, releasing and later attempting to recapture them (see DELANY, 1974).) By noting the relative age of sibling monkeys and the seasonality of sexual behaviour, it was deduced that there is a gap of one to two years between successive young. It is interesting to note that even though some males, the sub-adults, are fertile, they complete few copulations because their sexual behaviour is frequently interrupted by adult males. Similarly, a non-reproducing part of a population is found in many species: there are sterile workers in Hymenoptera, juveniles taking some years to mature in herring gulls, or males excluded from harems in polygynous species. There may be still other types of individuals present. In many ants there are three basic types of female *castes* (morphologically distinct sets of individuals specialized in behaviour): the queen for laying, workers for food gathering, brood care, nest construction, and soldiers for defence.

Another important demographic parameter is whether the animals are solitary or live in groups. If the latter is the case their composition must be discovered and whether they are societies, anonymous groups or aggregations. In the study of monkeys referred to above it took several months to be *sure* that the groups were multi-male societies with a regular membership and not just casual aggregations.

4.2.2   Population dispersion and spacing behaviour

Dispersion patterns   Animals living in an area do not use all the available habitat; they restrict their activities to particular places. The area an animal (or group of animals) uses during its routine daily activities is called the *home range*. Occasional forays or movements during migration are excluded. A home range is recorded by mapping where an animal goes. The dates and duration of the observations should be noted in case there are seasonal differences and to ensure that the observed home range is a good estimate of the true range for the period (Fig. 4–1). When we draw a line on our map enclosing all the records for an animal and call this its home range, we are of course making an abstraction. Animals live in a three-dimensional world, something our map does not allow for.

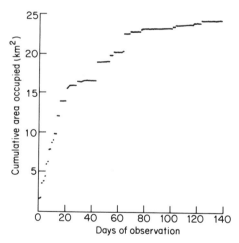

Fig. 4–1   The relationship between known home range size (cumulative area occupied) and days of observation for a group of common baboons. It took 70 days of observation before a good estimate of home range was obtained; after that time, new areas were entered infrequently. (From ALTMANN, S. A. and ALTMANN, J. (1970). *Baboon Ecology*. University of Chicago Press, Chicago.)

Note that the term 'home range' strictly implies nothing about the spatial or behavioural relations between neighbouring animals. When we examine how individuals (or groups) in a population space out their home ranges with reference to each other, we find a variety of *dispersion patterns*. The most widely known is territoriality but this is only one possibility. The key to understanding dispersion patterns is to refer to two features. (i) The *exclusiveness* of the individual (or group) home ranges: is an area used by only one individual (or group) or is it completely or partially used by others? (ii) The *spacing behaviour* shown: do animals *defend* all or part of their home range by threat, attack or intimidating advertisement (e.g. songs or scents) or do encounters take some other form? Interaction between these factors is illustrated in Fig. 4–2 which also gives examples. Remember that there is a continuum of dispersion patterns with intermediates between the kinds shown. At one extreme there is an almost complete overlap of non-exclusive home ranges with tolerance or avoidance between neighbours. At the other extreme the home range is a *territory* – 'a fixed area from which intruders are excluded by some combination of advertisement (e.g. scent, song), threat and attack' (BROWN, 1975).

The dispersion pattern shown by a population and home range size can be related to the size, anatomy, feeding habits, etc., of the animals and to the characteristics of the habitat (e.g. physical structure, quality and availability of food). These relationships and the function of territoriality are discussed in Chapter 8. It should be noted here, however, that territories may be classified as general purpose territories (used for all activities), mating territories (small areas used for courtship displays and mating), and nesting territories (small areas surrounding nests). For some animals it is easy to discover range size, exclusiveness and spacing behaviour. European robins are easy to watch and a breeding pair lives in a general purpose territory with a mean size of 0.6 ha (range 0.2–0.8 ha). It is very difficult to obtain equivalent information for small mammals, where range size and exclusiveness can be estimated from trapping (for methods see DELANY 1974), but spacing behaviour is almost impossible to see. For example, in woodmice (*Apodemus sylvaticus*) the females have home ranges (0.1–0.2 ha) with little overlap, while the breeding males have larger ranges (0.2–0.3 ha) that overlap the female ranges and may be territories.

All individuals or groups in a population may not have the same dispersion pattern. This is particularly conspicuous in some ungulates, for example in wildebeest and impala (*Aepyceros melampus*) during the mating season. In both species solitary adult males hold territories, while groups of females and young live in home ranges that overlap male territories. Each male attempts to court the females as they pass through his area. Non-territorial males, living chiefly in all-male groups, are largely excluded from territories and live in poorer habitats. Some may

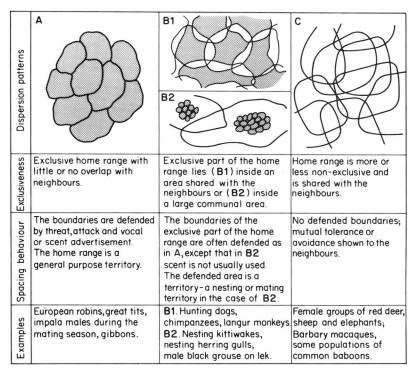

Dispersion patterns	A	B1 / B2	C
Exclusiveness	Exclusive home range with little or no overlap with neighbours.	Exclusive part of the home range lies (B1) inside an area shared with the neighbours or (B2) inside a large communal area.	Home range is more or less non-exclusive and is shared with the neighbours.
Spacing behaviour	The boundaries are defended by threat, attack and vocal or scent advertisement. The home range is a general purpose territory.	The boundaries of the exclusive part of the home range are often defended as in A, except that in B2 scent is not usually used. The defended area is a territory-a nesting or mating territory in the case of B2.	No defended boundaries; mutual tolerance or avoidance shown to the neighbours.
Examples	European robins, great tits, impala males during the mating season, gibbons.	B1. Hunting dogs, chimpanzees, langur monkeys. B2. Nesting kittiwakes, nesting herring gulls, male black grouse on lek.	Female groups of red deer, sheep and elephants; Barbary macaques, some populations of common baboons.

Fig. 4–2   Animal dispersion patterns and spacing behaviour. As explained in the text the dispersion patterns seen in nature vary between full territorial systems (A) and non-exclusive home ranges with mutual tolerance or avoidance between neighbours (C). B1 and B2 illustrate two of the intermediates in which animals have exclusive and non-exclusive parts to their home range. In each diagram several home ranges are represented by the lines and the exclusive parts of the home ranges are stippled.

be allowed within territories but they are subordinate to the territory owner and are not permitted to mate.

Irrespective of the dispersion pattern, animals rarely use all of their home range equally. Certain areas, called *core areas*, are used more heavily than others (Fig. 4–5) and may be linked by paths through otherwise unused terrain. In birds, the core area is likely to be a nest site; in carnivores, a den or resting place; in common baboons, sleeping trees, good feeding places or water holes. It is obviously only a short step from a core area to an exclusively used area or territory within a home range.

Territorial behaviour   This is an example of spacing behaviour and has been studied in numerous species and several generalizations can be made. (i) The behaviour is restricted to a particular locality, the territory, and often specifically to the territorial boundary. (ii) Opponents, males typically playing the major role, threaten each other using stereotyped postures. (iii) The aggressive nature of these postures is usually in little doubt since they are often punctuated with fights involving chases, attacks and flight. (iv) Between neighbours the outcome of a fight depends on its location, animals invariably win on their own ground; a completely strange intruder rarely beats a healthy territory owner. Three examples will demonstrate these points.

Territorial behaviour in white-handed gibbons In the white-handed gibbon each family sleeps near the centre of its small territory (mean size = 40 ha, range = 16–122 ha). When they wake at dawn they feed intensively and then at around 0700 h the adult female starts to give loud, booming 'great calls'. When a group calls near the territorial boundary its neighbouring group moves rapidly to the scene and vigorous display commences. Disputes, which go on almost daily throughout the year, are generally restricted to border areas. The females continue calling as the males swing around vigorously, calling, rushing at each other and chasing. Should one male catch another, shaking and biting clearly reveal the aggressive nature of these displays.

Territorial behaviour in great tits In contrast, territorial behaviour of the great tit is a seasonal affair. This bird, in common with other temperate passerines, establishes a territory in which to rear its young. Pairs formed in winter, gradually separate out from the flock and move independently around the flock's home range (see p. 35). When pairs meet, the males behave aggressively. Gradually a pair becomes attached to a particular place and the male sings vigorously and defends the area (mean size = 0.8 ha, range = 0.2–2 ha) against intruders, but the boundaries are not clearly defined until nest-building starts. Fights primarily involve males threatening and attacking each other (p. 48) but females may also be involved, particularly during the later stages of territory formation. It has been shown that a male's singing deters intruders. Territorial pairs were removed and the males' singing replaced with tape recordings of their songs. Resettlement of these territories by other pairs was delayed in comparison with similar territories without replacement song (Fig. 4–3).

Territorial behaviour in black-headed gulls The gulls provide some of the most detailed descriptions of territorial behaviour since their small nesting territories make observation relatively easy. Black-headed gulls winter away from the nesting grounds. As they return they gather near the colony site squabbling and courting, some pairs being formed. Pairs and birds still unpaired start to visit the colony site, landing and fighting. Birds which arrive paired are most successful, soon becoming attached to a particular area – their new territory – and vigorously defending it. As an intruding male lands, the territory owner (whether paired or not) immediately rushes forward in attack and the intruder rapidly leaves: threat displays are rarely used. In contrast, squabbles

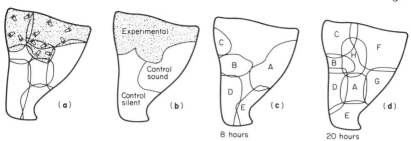

Fig. 4–3 Experimental investigation of the role of great tit song in deterring intruders. (a) Shows the positions of the territory boundaries in the wood before the start of the experiment. The three experimental territories are stippled and the approximate positions of the loudspeakers are shown. (b) Shows how the wood was divided up into experimental, control sound, and control silent territories. In the control sound territories, the loudspeakers broadcast a two-note phrase similar to the song of a great tit, but played on a tin whistle. (c) and (d) show the progress of reoccupation of the wood by new birds. The number of hours on each map refers to the number of daylight hours since the start of the experiment (about 9½ h per day). The letters in each territory refer to the sequence in which new birds arrived. (From KREBS, J. (1976). Bird song and territorial defence. *New Scientist*, **72**, 534–6. This just appeared in *New Scientist*, London, the weekly review of science and technology.)

between neighbours may involve more display. The behaviour shown depends on the precise location; males are more aggressive inside their territories, becoming more intimidated and more likely to flee as they move over the boundary. Two of the postures used are illustrated in Fig. 4–4. The aggressive upright posture clearly shows elements of attack; the bill is pointed down ready for striking and the wings are raised for beating. The displaying bird advances towards its opponent. The intimidated upright posture is adopted by a more fearful bird who does not face its opponent. Although at first the female plays little part in territorial defence she gradually starts to join her mate in this activity.

Fig. 4–4 Two of the postures adopted by black-headed gulls: left, aggressive upright; right, intimidated upright. (From TINBERGEN (1974.)

Territorial fighting and other fights   What is the relationship between
territorial fighting and other fights by which social rank is established in
other circumstances (p. 59)? Territorial fighting is simply a special case,
since it relates to obtaining and defending a *specific locality* for the
resources (food, water, nest site, females, etc.) it makes available. It also
involves fighting between solitary animals or societies and not between
animals within societies. The winners get the best territories, losers the
poorest or none at all. Whether an animal gets a territory or not, and also
the quality of the territory, will depend on population density, the
availability and defensibility of suitable resources, and also on the
animal's health and age (p. 90). Experimental manipulation of these
variables in the laboratory has shown that it is possible to change the
proportion of territorial/non-territorial animals. In animals as diverse as
impala, mice and cockroaches (*Nauphoeta cinerea*), territorial males may
actively exclude each other but may tolerate a few subordinate non-
territorial males in their territory. They are simultaneously showing
territorial and hierarchial relationships. Territorial animals are
dominant on their own ground. When they are tested off their territory, as
might happen when great tits fight on a garden bird table, animals closest
to their territory tend to win most fights.

Other spacing behaviour   Territorial defence can be so spectacular that it
is easy to overlook other spacing behaviour and its associated dispersion
patterns. An interesting case is provided by South American howling
monkeys (*Alouatta palliata*) in which neighbouring groups rarely
meet; they assess each other's position from their daily, early morning
howls. Groups that are close tend to move apart after calling and so keep
to their own areas. Many mammals rely on scent to register their
individual or group identity with their neighbours. Typically, scented
glandular secretions are rubbed onto objects or deposited with the urine
or faeces. In rabbits (*Oryctolagus cuniculus*) each group's territory has a
characteristic smell to which strangers entering the territory soon
respond. The highest ranking males in each warren are the most active
markers, depositing piles of scented pellets within their territory and
around its perimeter. Conspicuous objects are also marked using a gland
under the chin. So-called 'territorial' marking has been reported from
other species – lions, wolves, European hamsters (*Cricetus cricetus*), gerbils
(*Meriones unguiculatus*) and domestic dogs, to name just a few. Mammals
will, however, mark under all sorts of circumstances (e.g. in response to
novelty, and in association with sexual and aggressive behaviour) and
marking clearly has many functions. The term 'territorial marking' must
be applied with caution (see STODDART, 1976).

The mutual tolerance or avoidance shown between neighbours in the
non-exclusive parts of their home ranges has not attracted the same
attention as territorial fighting. Groups of mountain gorillas (*Gorilla
gorilla*) show little response when they meet and serious fighting is not

seen. They live in overlapping home ranges of 26–39 km². Similarly, common baboons tend to avoid other groups. If they meet, overt fighting is rare and several groups may visit a water hole in peace, a small group slowly avoiding a larger one.

4.2.3   Intragroup social behaviour

The third component of this description of social organization is a knowledge of how animals interact with other members of their group. We must know how they communicate, cooperate and compete; how these activities develop, how they are distributed with age and between the sexes. The next three chapters are devoted to these questions.

4.2.4   Changes in the above features with time

Social organization is not static – an individual's relations with other group members are constantly modified as are the relations between groups. Under seasonal conditions reproduction occurs at the optimal time and there are often marked seasonal changes in social organization. Each distinct pattern of social organization is called a *social phase*. In great tits we see a change between a breeding territorial phase in spring and summer, and a flocking phase in autumn and winter (p. 35). In red deer there is a non-reproductive phase involving loose all-male groups and more cohesive female groups, and a mating-season phase during which temporary harems are formed. Changes may even occur on an hourly basis. On cold days in spring, pairs of great tits may visit their territories in the morning but they tend to reassemble in flocks during the afternoon. The seasonal changes in social behaviour are directly related to changes in reproductive physiology (Fig. 7–5) and the demands that reproduction places on the organism. Each change of social phase involves the three features discussed above: demography, dispersion and intragroup behaviour. In tits, for example, the change from the flocking to territorial phase includes decreasing tolerance of others, reduced movements, increased attachment to and defence of an area, mate selection and the development of the close cooperation between mates so essential for successful reproduction. An important characteristic of most non-human primate societies and those of some other mammals (e.g. lions) is their *lack* of seasonal phases in social organization. There may be seasonal changes in mating and other behaviour but for the most part population dispersion and spacing behaviour are stable. The long-term association of individuals is an important feature of their social life and as we saw earlier (p. 22) this permits the development of matrilineal genealogies.

Perhaps some of the greatest changes in social organization occur when new societies are formed. In wasps and bumble-bees (*Bombus*) each colony is founded in spring by a single fertilized female who hibernated through the previous winter. Gradually the colony is built up, daughters acting as workers. Only late in the season are males and new queens produced to complete the annual cycle. In contrast, the honeybee has developed food storage and with it the ability of the colony to overwinter and found powerful new colonies by swarming.

We shall see later that major changes in many aspects of social organization can be directly related to changing ecological conditions (Chapter 8). The part played by an individual in its social organization also changes as it matures and competes with its peers and elders to maximize its chances of reproduction.

4.3 Some examples of social organization

4.3.1 Honeybees (Apis mellifera)

A colony in summer consists of a reproductive female (queen), several thousand sterile females (workers), and a few hundred fertile males (drones) and the brood. It occupies a natural or artificial (e.g. hive) chamber in which wax comb is constructed to house the brood and stores of pollen and honey. The drones, who do little apart from fertilizing queens on mating flights, are killed in autumn and the overwintering colony consists of the queen and workers living on the stored food. Egg production starts again in the spring. The queen may be mated by several males on a single mating flight and stores their sperm. She normally lays fertilized eggs (diploid) that produce females. Eggs hatch into larvae after three days and are fed for five days, after which they pupate in a cocoon inside their wax cell. The adult worker emerges 21 days after the egg was laid, queens a few days earlier, drones a few days later. Larvae are normally given a diet of 'royal jelly' (secreted by the workers) for two days and then increasing quantities of honey. With this diet the larvae develop into sterile females (workers). Unfertilized eggs from the queen produce drones which are consequently haploid. The importance of this haplo-diploid system was discussed earlier (p. 14). The queen produces chemical signals (pheromones) that inhibit the workers from rearing new queens and prevent them from laying eggs. Should the queen die or become too old, the workers rear a new queen by feeding a larva on royal jelly (and in contrast to workers, little honey). Without the pheromone inhibition, some workers lay unfertilized eggs producing drones. New queens are also produced under other circumstances and the old queen then swarms with some of the workers to establish a new colony. The workers do everything in the colony apart from laying eggs. In mid-summer they live for only 4–6 weeks and their activities are in part controlled by age: 0–3 days old, cleaning cells and keeping brood warm; 3–6, feeding older larvae; 6–14, feeding younger larvae and queen; 14–18, secreting wax, comb-building and cleaning hive; 18–20, guarding entrance; 20–40, foraging for pollen and honey. This is not a rigid schedule and it is modified according to the needs of the colony. For example, if the hive is too hot, foragers switch to collecting water which is then used for evaporative cooling in the hive. The dances used by foragers to communicate the direction and distance to food are described on p. 46.

4.3.2   Great tits (Parus major)

The great tit lives in mixed woodland throughout Europe and Asia. The following account is based on studies conducted near Oxford. During the winter the birds move in loose flocks of about 12 birds (but sometimes containing up to 50) which often include additional birds of other species. They feed on insects, spiders, seeds and fruits. The flocks occupy slightly overlapping, undefended home ranges of about 4 ha (for a flock of 12). Flocking increases a bird's chance of finding food (p. 81) but there is also considerable fighting over food, one bird threatening or attacking another and taking the food that it found. In January–March, this flocking phase of the social organization gives way to the territorial phase. Pair formation takes place in the winter flocks and the pair spends more and more time away from the flock, returning to it during the afternoons and during spells of cold weather. Each pair sets up a territory (well defined by late March) as described earlier (p. 30). Suitable nest sites, usually holes in a tree are inspected by the male, and the female is attracted by his behaviour. The female builds the nest and a clutch of 5–11 eggs are laid in late April or early May. During building, copulation and laying, the close cooperation established between the pair continues. The male feeds the female, a vital contribution to offset the burden of egg-laying. Incubation is by the female alone, but the male continues to feed her. The eggs, and later the young, are liable to predation by grey squirrels (Neosciurus carolinensis) and weasels (Mustela nivalis) against which the parents have little defence. The young hatch, are fed by both parents (largely on caterpillars), and fly when 18–20 days old (June–July). On average, six young are reared per pair. They are still fed by the parents after leaving the nest but are largely independent of them within two weeks. The young birds fight a lot and many disappear from the population. In September–October there is a revival of territorial behaviour but as the winter approaches, flocks are reformed. Adults are sedentary and live near their summer territories but juveniles may disperse up to several kilometres before joining flocks. Mortality (which mainly occurs in the summer and autumn) varies considerably from year to year and seems to be related to the food supply. About 17% of the new juveniles survive to the following breeding season (i.e. one out of the six young reared on average by each pair), but the adult survival rate is 50%.

4.3.3   Red deer (Cervus elaphus)

The following description is based on animals living on the moorlands of the Scottish Highlands and islands. Outside the rut the population is divided into female groups (varying in size, according to the locality, from ten to several hundred individuals) and smaller, less stable, all-male groups. The female groups consist of adult females and their young, including males up to three years old. Females occupy overlapping home ranges (about 4 km²) and the groups frequently divide into matrilineal sub-groups which, since they can live for up to 20 years, can contain three or more generations of females with their young. Under the leadership of one of the older females, they move around their home range, the part utilized depending on the weather. At three years the young males leave their mothers and join all-male groups. Adult males have ranges (about 8 km²) that tend to be peripheral to, and slightly overlapping with the female ranges. In the all-male groups, each male's status depends on his bulk and the size of his antlers. During the rut, starting in late September (see Fig. 7–5) the males become aggressive towards each other and the group splits up, each male moving to its favoured rutting area. Individual males compete with other males to gain possession of females. A male constantly roars, herds his harem of 10–20 females and their calves, and defends it from other males. Females are generally fertile in their third year. The most effective males are seven and more years old but even these become exhausted with rutting, losing 25% of their body weight, and are eventually driven off by competing males. The male does not act as the leader of his harem and leaves it in times of danger. After the rut, the female group/all-male group situation is restored. The antlers (present only in the male) are shed in spring (Fig. 7–5) but new ones start to grow immediately. Before giving birth (May–June) the female leaves her group, drives away her young of previous years and finds a secluded spot. Calves hide for the first 7–10 days, their mothers returning to feed them. They then move with their mothers, who subsequently rejoin the group. Suckling continues for 8–10 months.

4.3.4   Common baboons (Papio cynocephalus)

There are several varieties of baboons, living in Africa south of the Sahara, which may be grouped together under this specific name. (The sacred baboon (*P. hamadryas*), described on p. 86, is *not* included.) This description applies to savanna animals, there being considerable differences in forest and arid populations (p. 89). The population is divided into multi-male groups of 20–200 animals (mean=45) with generally more adult females than adult males. There are no solitaries. The groups are permanent and cohesive, except that young adult males usually change groups. Group structure does not change seasonally. Groups occupy large (up to 40 km²) overlapping home ranges (Fig. 4–5), meet infrequently and tend to avoid each other. Each night the group sleeps in tall trees (or on a rock face) away from predators. At dawn they descend and their day of moving and feeding starts. A large proportion of the time is spent searching for food and the group fans out across the savanna. Typically the younger males are more peripheral than the

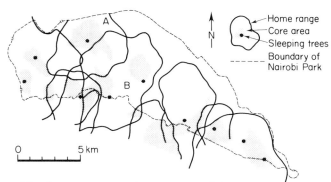

Fig. 4–5 The home ranges and core areas of the nine groups of common baboons in Nairobi Park. The ranges of only two groups are considered complete (A = 24 km²; B = 40 km²) and so the overlap is even more extensive than indicated. (After DEVORE, I. and HALL, K. R. L. (1965). In: *Primate Behaviour*, I. DeVore (Ed.). Holt, Rinehart and Winston, New York, 20–52.)

females and their young. Adult males may confront minor predators but they more usually flee to safety with the rest of the group. Females (mature at five years) are only receptive for a few days of their monthly menstrual cycle. Individual females spend most of their time pregnant or lactating but, because their reproduction is not seasonal, some females are available for mating most of the time. The males (fully mature at ten years) compete for access to the females who are promiscuous. Because of this competition, the young males only manage to copulate at the sub-optimal parts of the females' receptive period. Mothers suckle their young for 6–8 months and carry them until they are old enough to move independently. The males play little part in rearing the young. As in macaques (Fig. 3–2), a matrilineal kin system provides the core to the group and much social interaction takes place between relatives. Baboons cannot recognize their fathers. There is a social hierarchy (p. 61) and a wide variety of social interaction (e.g. grooming, threatening, fighting and playing). Young females help care for their younger siblings, around whom a lot of the social behaviour revolves. Much social behaviour is learnt, or at least develops, only in a setting where social practice is possible. There is a sub-culture in which groups have traditional sleeping and watering places; information on the utilization of the environment is apparently stored in the older animals, who can live for perhaps 20 years.

4.3.5 Chimpanzees (Pan troglodytes)

Chimpanzees live in equatorial Africa, mainly in forested habitats. They have been intensively studied in the Gombe Stream Reserve, Tanzania on which this account is based. Their social organization is not fully understood. The society is not a cohesive group; it has a more open group structure in which small temporary parties of up to six individuals (more, if food is abundant) move around together, often splitting and rejoining. The parties can be composed of any combination of the different age–sex classes of animals in the population, with the exception that young travel with their mothers. Lone animals are also often seen. In spite of this fluidity, it is thought that within an area of forest the individuals making up the temporary parties are members of a multi-male-type community of up to 40 individuals. Unlike its baboon counterpart, however, this never moves as a complete unit. The major evidence for this community structure is that within any one area the same individuals are repeatedly seen but in different combinations, and in an adjacent area the same applies to the animals that make up the neighbouring community. Each community is thought to have a home range of 10–20 km², parts of which are defended by bloody (and sometimes fatal) skirmishes, chiefly between males. Within the range the individual males and females have preferred areas.

The above summary implies that a specific set of females associate with a specific set of males, but some observers would argue that there is little evidence for such associations. What is certain, however, is that the most persistent relationship in chimpanzees is based on the matrilineal genealogy: animals descended from the same mother move together until adolescence (nine years old). In some cases a male may monopolize a female in oestrus, but there is no long-term pair-bonding and promiscuity is typical. The animals make nests to sleep in at night but have no permanent base or den. Mothers therefore carry their young continuously, mother–infant contact not being broken for at least the first three months. The period of maternal dependence is extraordinary; suckling continues for three to four and a half years. Chimpanzees have a comprehensive system of communication using facial expressions, body postures, calls, touching hands and embracing (Fig. 5–2). Play is important in young animals, grooming in older ones. Males show vigorous aggressive displays and can be ranked in a hierarchy. Chimpanzees travel about 3–4 km per day, mainly on the ground, and are largely vegetarian. Mammals are, however, caught and eaten, and termites and ants fished for with sticks fashioned for the job. Sticks and stones are also used in defence. The longevity in the wild is unknown but could be as long as 40 years. Females probably first become pregnant when they are at least ten years old. Males mate from seven years upwards but do not reach the full stature of adulthood until about 14 years old.

5 Communication Between Individuals

5.1 What is communication?

In the present context we can define *communication* as the passing of information from one animal to another (and so influencing its behaviour) by means of signals that have evolved for the purpose. *Information* includes any statement about the environment or the signaller's identity, physiology or intentions. A *signal* is a structure, chemical or behavioural event that has been *adapted* for communication, for example bird song, a male stickleback's red belly, a monkey's facial expression. The study of communication is central to the study of social behaviour since social behaviour depends on animals being able to communicate with each other. Communication takes many forms involving different senses, circumstances and various kinds of information. Examples of the senses used include hearing (e.g. vocalizations and the sounds produced by wing vibration in fruit flies, Fig. 5–1), smell and taste (scent trails of ants, urine marks and the honeybee queen pheromone, touch (hand-shaking in humans and hand-touching in chimpanzees, Fig. 5–2), and sight (facial expressions, body postures and patches of colourful plumage and skin).

Much animal communication involves a complex patterning of signals and other stimuli. This can easily be seen by watching two dogs meeting; visual, vocal and olfactory signals are used as the dogs weigh each other

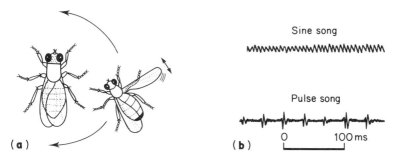

Sine song

Pulse song

0   100 ms

Fig. 5–1 Wing vibration of courting male *Drosophila melanogaster*. (a) As he courts the female (left) the male holds his wing out and vibrates the tip. (From BASTOCK, M., 1967.) (b) Oscilloscope traces of the sound pulses produced by the wing vibration. The functional significance of the differences between the two 'song' types is unknown. (From SCHILCHER, F. VON (1976). *Anim. Behav.*, **24**, 18–26.)

Fig. 5–2 Tactile communication in chimpanzees. A mother (carrying her new-born ventrally), apprehensively approaches three adult males. She holds out her hand to one of them who touches it. (After LAWICK-GOODALL, J. VAN (1968). *Anim. Behav. Monogr.*, **1** (3).

up. It is clearly artificial to look at one signal or one response without relating it to other events.

5.1.1 The communication process

While retaining a respect for the complexity of our subject we can break up the communication process as follows: (i) the state of the signaller; (ii) making the signal; (iii) signal reception; and (iv) the influence of the signal on the recipient's behaviour. Each step will be considered in turn.

The state of the signaller The start of a communicative act lies hidden from our view and is influenced by the signaller's internal state or *motivation*. If an animal is sexually aroused, fearful or hungry then this will affect the signals it produces. Some signals, such as bird song and the sounds made by male grasshoppers to attract mates, seem to be largely controlled by internal events. Signals may, however, be influenced to a greater extent by external stimuli: on sighting a predator a black-bird calls and rushes for cover. The relevant external stimuli are frequently signals received from other individuals. For example, when a singing male zebra finch (*Taeniopygia guttata*) approaches a receptive female in a tail-twisting display she responds with tail-quivering (Fig. 5–3). Examples from human behaviour include the almost automatic response of a wave to a wave, a smile to a smile. Immediate, stereotyped responses do not, however, invariably occur, as will be shown below.

Making the signal The extent to which animals direct signals at each other varies. The signaller's behaviour is clearly *directed* at the recipient when a black-headed gull threatens another at a territorial boundary, or when it rushes at an intruder. In other cases signals may be *broadcast* as with bird song, gibbon great calls and the release of scent into the atmosphere by female moths attracting mates. These signals are used by animals to announce their presence over long distances. Using the receptors on his very large antennae the male gipsy moth (*Lymantria dispar*) can detect a female at over 1000 m. In other cases animals attach their signals to the environment: worker ants lay down scent trails to guide others to and from food and, as was shown earlier (p. 32), male rabbits rub scent onto objects around their warren (see STODDART, 1976).

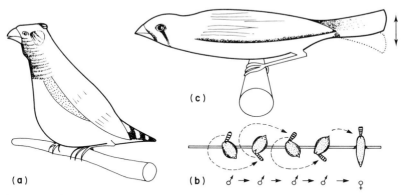

(c)

(a)   (b)   ♂ → ♂ → ♂ → ♂ → ♀

Fig. 5–3   The courtship dance of the male zebra finch. The male, in the upright courtship posture (a), sings vigorously and dances towards the female, pivoting from side to side (b). A receptive female adopts the tail quivering display (c) and the male mounts her. (From MORRIS, D. (1954). *Behaviour*, 6, 271–322.)

Signal reception   To receive a signal the recipient must have sense organs matched to the signal; details of these cannot be given here, or of the subsequent neural events (see MESSENGER, 1979).

The influence of the signal on the recipient's behaviour   The influence of the signal on the recipient's behaviour depends (like signal generation) on *motivational factors* hidden from view. Consider the following example: when a herring gull approaches its nest to feed the young chicks, it stretches its neck downwards and utters a long 'mew call'. The chicks respond by becoming alert and running to the parent who regurgitates half-digested food. The parent picks up small pieces and holds them between the tips of the bill for the chicks to take. The mew call signal is not *always* followed by the chicks approaching; chicks that are not hungry do not respond. In cases such as this we assume that the recipient got the *message* (i.e. the information about the signaller's state) but that its own internal state (motivation) resulted in the full response not being made.

It frequently happens that an animal's response to a signal also depends on the *context* – the immediate situation in which the animal finds itself. We can therefore say that the *meaning* of the message coded in the signal depends on the context in which the signal is received and *not the signal alone*. For example, if a macaque monkey has been threatened it may step

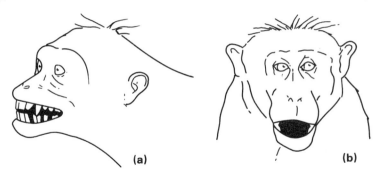

Fig. 5–4   Facial expressions of Bonnet macaque monkeys (*Macaca radiata*). (a) Staring bared-teeth scream face – a submissive expression given by a screaming and fearful animal in which the lips are withdrawn and the ears are flattened. (b) Staring open-mouth face – a threatening expression. (From MARLER, P. (1965). In: *Primate Behaviour*, I. DeVore (Ed.). Holt, Rinehart and Winston, New York, 544–84.)

back and vigorously scream while giving the bared-teeth scream face (Fig. 5–4). The message conveyed to the threatener is 'fear' and the meaning in this context is 'submission' and 'non-aggression'. Sometimes the screaming monkey elicits another's help by alternating repeatedly between looking at the threatener and at a higher-ranking monkey who happens to be nearby. Under these circumstances the latter monkey often runs to the screamer's aid against the original threatener. Although using basically the same signal its meaning is different and can be stated anthropomorphically as 'help me against my aggressor'. Other signals illustrate the same point. The presenting posture is used by female monkeys soliciting copulation (Fig. 7–1), by both sexes to appease an attacker and indicate submission and as a greeting. The honeybees' tail-wagging dance is also used in two contexts: it directs workers to food and a swarm to a new nest site. Clearly, the recipient responds to a signal in context and it is this that determines the meaning. A word of caution is perhaps pertinent: to be certain that this argument holds one must be sure that the signal *is* the same in both contexts. This can be difficult to establish.

5.1.2   *Testing the communicative value of signals*

We judge that communication has occurred when a signal changes the *probability* that the recipient will give a certain behaviour. This is what is implied when we note that after hearing a warning call a bird is more likely to flee, or that a worker bee is more likely to visit a particular crop of flowers if it was present when another forager gave the tail-wagging-dance. Experimental manipulations can be used to test the com-municative value of probable signals. Signals, in the form of tape-recorded calls or models emphasizing particular aspects of a signal, can be presented and changes in the probability of the recipient's behaviour recorded. An example of this is provided by a series of experiments investigating the stimuli that elicit begging in newly-hatched herring gull chicks. We have seen above how the parents use the mew call to attract the chicks. By presenting to the chicks painted cardboard models of an adult's head it was shown that the stimulating aspects of the parent's display involves a combination of movement, definite shape, 'lowness', 'nearness', pointing downwards, a red patch on the bill tip characterized by colour and contrast, and something (in nature, food) protruding outside the bill's outline. While these features all contribute to the display, the red spot on the bill is the only true *signal* present by virtue of the fact that it appears to have evolved for purposes of communication.

It can also be useful to remove signals and then to record what happens. One example was given earlier; eliminating the song of territorial great tits results in their territories being invaded sooner than in equivalent territories supplied with tape-recorded calls (Fig. 4–3). In a very different study, the plumage of male red-winged blackbirds was altered in order to investigate its signal function. Males of this American species establish small, clearly defined territories which they defend by means of combined singing and posturing (the so-called 'song-spread' display) and by chasing. During the display, conspicuous wing epaulets of red feathers bordered with yellow are erected. Some blackbirds were caught and experimental birds had their epaulets dyed black, while control birds had their epaulets wiped with alcohol. Within five minutes of release the birds returned to their territories where they were observed. Subsequently, 92% of the control males but only 36% of the black-epaulet males retained their territories (Table 2). The majority of the experimental birds losing territories did so within two days of the dyeing. Intruding birds failed to respond to the territory owners' postures and song, thus demonstrating the importance of the epaulet signal.

Table 2   The effect of altering the epaulets of male red-winged blackbirds (*Agelaius phoeniceus*) on the maintenance of their territories. (After SMITH, D. G. (1972) *Behaviour*, 41, 251–68.)

	Normal males (control birds)	Males with black epaulets
Maintained territory	37 (92%)	17 (36%)
Lost territory	3 (8%)	30 (64%)
Status in question*	4	10

* Refers to birds who could not be observed clearly owing to the difficult terrain and vegetation.

Female red-winged blackbirds are dull in comparison with males, a feature shared with many birds including chaffinches. Males chaffinches have a reddish-orange throat and breast and the importance of this feature was investigated by dyeing females. The results were conclusive: dyed females won more encounters, the other females treated them like males (Table 3).

Table 3   The effect of disguising female chaffinches as males. In each experiment, two females whose breast feathers had been dyed red were matched with two normal females whose breast feathers had been treated with dilute soap solution as a control. (From MARLER, P. (1955). *British Journal of Animal Behaviour*, 3, 137–46.)

Result of aggressive encounters	Experiment number					Total
	1	2	3	4	5	
'Red' female wins	75	71	42	92	71	351
Normal female wins	29	11	25	5	0	70
Percentage of 'red' wins	72	87	63	95	100	83

5.1.3   Incidental communication

In the definition of communication (p. 39) it was emphasized that we were considering signals that have evolved for communicative purposes. The importance of this statement can be illustrated by looking at cases where information is *inadvertently* passed between animals. If a colony of great blue herons (*Ardea herodias*) at their nests high in a clump of trees is observed and a bird is seen flying in and feeding its young and when it leaves on another feeding trip, a neighbour takes off and appears to follow it to the feeding grounds, can we say that one bird communicated the presence of food to the other? Probably not, since the follower's action depended on it *interpreting* the behaviour of the other and *not* on a signal that evolved to convey the message 'this way to food'. The same problems arise when one looks at apparent communication *between* species. It would be wrong to say that a worm communicates its presence by wriggling to a bird who then eats it; the worm's wriggling has not evolved to attract birds. On the other hand, Hymenoptera such as wasps are unpleasant to eat and they signal this by their bright yellow and black stripes. This can be considered a case of inter-specific communication, since there is good evidence (CARTHY, 1979) that their distinctive colouration was evolved as a signal. The distinction we are making in all cases is between an *evolved adaptation*, in which the animal has an 'intent' to communicate, and an *incidental effect*. Given the appropriate conditions the latter could of course evolve into a signal (p. 49).

5.1.4   Signals in monkey courtship

To illustrate some of the complexities and characteristics of signals we

can look at the sexual behaviour of macaques and baboons. Imagine that
the monkeys are being watched and that an adult male is quietly feeding.
An adult female with a swollen and colourful bottom approaches, glances
at him and, as she gets closer turns and presents. He looks at her swelling,
places his nose close to her genitalia and then turns and feeds. The female,
moving away a little, also feeds. To fully understand this sequence,
further observations would have to be made. It would be seen that the
interactions could also be started by a male approaching a female, and
that in some cases sniffing is followed by mounting and copulation.

During this sequence the female gives signals involving colour and
shape (the colourful swelling), stereotyped posturing (presenting to the
male) and an odour produced in her vagina. She also conveys information to the male in other ways, by her relaxed and direct approach,
and by looking at him without any particular facial expression. The male
will also know her as an individual and will have knowledge of her past
behaviour. These additional features provide useful back-up information
for the recipient. The whole sequence of signals and associated behaviour
shown by the female make up a *display* (see p. 4). Other examples of
displays have been given earlier – the territorial displays of black-headed
gulls and gibbons. Note that the term 'display' is frequently also used as a
synonym of 'signal'.

The female's swelling is a *graded* signal since it has many forms.
Swellings may be flat, slightly swollen, swollen or grossly swollen at
different stages of the menstrual cycle, and they also vary in colour. Many
monkey calls are also graded signals: by using intermediate calls, in
combination with different expressions and orientations of the body, a
monkey has an infinitely flexible *communication system* which can convey
very subtle changes in mood. In contrast, many signals are *discrete*, and
highly stereotyped, for example male fireflies flashing their light signals at
regular intervals, minimize ambiguity but only at a loss of the subtlety
provided by graded signals.

Pursuing the monkey example further, it should be noted that the
female does not constantly show courtship displays. On a daily basis there
will be periods, shortly after copulation, when she no longer displays; in
any one month, displays will be concentrated towards the middle of the
menstrual cycle when she is likely to ovulate (the time of oestrus); and in
any one year, she may only display for two or three months since at other
times she will be pregnant or lactating. Clearly her behaviour is affected
by underlying motivational factors, in this case her hormonal condition.

5.1.5   *Sign stimuli and releasers*

So far, signals have been emphasized within the context of a display,
but it can sometimes be shown that only one signal in the display is of
prime importance. A robin will attack a bunch of red feathers as if it were
a real rival; a male stickleback will attack a crude fish model with a red

belly more than a life-like model without one. Signals that act in this way are called *sign stimuli*. The term *releaser* has also been used to emphasize that the stimulus invariably releases a particular response. Signal specificity is highest in invertebrates: in primates and other animals, where responses are more variable and more dependent on experience and context, these terms are less valuable.

5.2   The functions of communication

5.2.1   *Information about the environment*

When a hawk flies near a group of foraging starlings, the first bird to see it gives a harsh squawk and the flock immediately takes to the wing. In this case the signal (the squawk) conveys information about the *environment* (the presence of a predator) as well as the caller's fear. Environmental information of a very different sort is conveyed by the nest-showing display of the yellowhammer (*Emberiza citrinella*). The male indicates a suitable site to his female by running to it with nest material, calling softly and quivering his wings while holding his body horizontal.

The well-known honeybee dances provide a most intriguing example. When a foraging worker has found a food source it signals this to other workers on its return to the hive. If the food source is close to the hive (less than 25 m away) the forager performs the *round dance* on the comb (Fig. 5–5). Other workers are attracted and recruited to forage on flowers with the same scent as that carried by the dancer. At distances greater than 100 m, the *tail-wagging* dance is used (Fig. 5–5). As fully explained in FREE, (1977), this dance carries information on the direction and distance to the food. The method used to communicate distance to the bees that follow the dancer, is a good example of a graded signal. Short and frequent wagging runs, with a low number of waggles per run, signal short distances (e.g. 9 runs per 15 s indicates about 100 m); longer and hence less frequent runs, with a higher number of waggles per run, signal longer distances (e.g. 2.5 runs per 15 s indicates about 4000 m). Bees following the dancer touch her with their antennae and are given food. Both dances are conducted in the dark and communication must therefore be by vibration, touch or odour.

5.2.2   *Information about the internal state*

Some signals convey information about an animal's *internal state* and, correspondingly, about what it is likely to do next. As we have already seen the black-headed gull's upright posture indicates aggressiveness and the female monkey's presentation signals her readiness to mate. Other signals communicate fear and submissiveness and may also have an appeasing function, by reducing the tendency of the recipient to attack the signaller.

Sequence analysis   What methods are used to discover the functions of

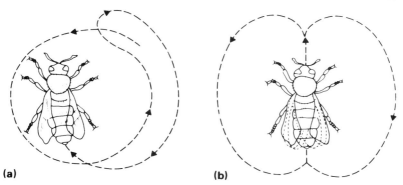

(a)   **(b)**

Fig. 5–5. Honeybee dances. (a) The round dance in which the bee makes a series of alternately clockwise and anti-clockwise circular movements on the comb. (b) The tail-wagging dance in which a figure of eight pattern is made. The abdomen is waggled during the straight run between the loops. (From FRISCH, K. VON (1950). *Bees: Their Vision, Chemical Senses, and Language.* Cornell University Press, New York, and Jonathan Cape, London.)

signals and displays? Good clues are provided by the form of the display itself. The black-headed gull's upright posture includes elements used in attack (the raised head with downwards pointing beak and the flexed wings) and so it is fair to guess that this posture is aggressive. This casual form of analysis is often insufficient and a more detailed quantitative approach is required. In a study of black mangabey monkeys in a tropical forest, the behaviour associated with staring was recorded. A staring monkey looks at its opponent with eyes open wide, eyebrows raised, mouth slightly open, corners of the lips slightly forwards and the teeth covered. When sitting it leans forwards; when standing it frequently crouches and may dart at the opponent. In the light of the behaviour which follows staring (Table 4), we can justifiably call the expression a threat. It is associated in the signaller with a tendency to attack and it is usually followed by retreat of the recipient. There is a problem with this type of analysis – it is difficult to be sure that all aspects of the display are constant from one case to another. While each incident included a stare, was the monkey's posture and orientation to the recipient constant? Were the events that preceded the stare constant?

Similar methods were used to analyse the displays of fighting great tits. Rather than study their behaviour during territorial fighting (p. 30) it was convenient to attract them to a bird table where experiments and close observation were possible. Three conspicuous displays which seemed aggressive were recognized – 'head-up', 'horizontal' and 'head-down'. After a bird had given a display its subsequent behaviour was recorded. The results showed that each display was associated with different

Table 4   Behaviour that follows staring in black mangabeys (*Cercocebus albigena*). (Note that the behaviour of the recipient was recorded in fewer cases than that of the starer and so the row totals do not agree.) (Data from CHALMERS, N. R. (1968). *Folia Primatol.*, **9**, 258–80.)

Behaviour shown after a stare	Attack	Stay (or approach*)	Flee
By the starer	6	12	0
By the recipient of the stare	0	2	12

* Scored only for the recipients of stares.

probabilities of attacking and fleeing and, therefore, reflected slight changes in motivation. 'Head-down' was more likely to be followed by attack and less likely to be followed by fleeing, than 'head-up' (Table 5). The different communicative value of these postures was revealed by other observations which showed that they were responded to differently.

These examples illustrate the technique of *sequence analysis* which can be a powerful tool in the analysis of social behaviour. Two types of sequences can be recognized: (*a*) sequences *within* the behaviour of an individual (e.g. a great tit giving 'head-up' following this with attack); and (*b*) sequences in the behaviour *between* individuals (e.g. staring in one monkey being followed by retreat in another). In a social situation these two types of sequences interact: if a stare is followed by the signaller attacking, is the attack a response to some action of the recipient of the

Table 5   Threat postures of great tits and the behaviour shown by birds after they have given each posture. The behaviour of the opponent is not taken into account. (Data and drawings from BLURTON JONES, N. G. (1968). *Anim. Behav. Monogr.*, **1**, 75–158.)

Posture	Behaviour shown by bird after it had given the postures listed on the left				
	Attack	Approach	Neither	Flee	Total
Head-down	50 (14%)	100 (27%)	189 (52%)	27 (7%)	366
Horizontal	35 (18%)	23 (12%)	106 (55%)	30 (15%)	194
Head-up	29 (6%)	61 (14%)	267 (60%)	90 (20%)	447

stare, or is it independent of external stimuli? Factors like this are difficult to tease apart.

5.2.3 Further functions of communication

Animals communicate other things, besides information on the environment and their internal state. Further functions include communicating location, identity (individual birds often have slightly different songs), sex (many animals signal sexual differences by colours or structures such as antlers), and group identity (animals such as mice and social insects have group odours). Finally, signals are used to coordinate the behaviour of animals cooperating in a task such as mating or rearing young. Extreme examples of this are seen when signals have a stimulating effect on the gonads, and so prepare the recipient for reproduction. One such case, the effect of male courtship on the reproductive system of the female ring dove (*Streptopelia risoria*), is explained in detail by SLATER (1978).

5.3 Communication and evolution

5.3.1 The origin of signals

One question that immediately comes to mind when we see animals displaying is: how have such complex displays with their associated structures and colours evolved? We must restrict ourselves to two aspects of this problem – the origin of signals from other activities, and the environmental and other selection pressures that have influenced the form of signals and displays.

A commonly held view is that behaviour from non-social situations has gradually taken on a communicative function. Many signals, for example, involve *intention movements* of locomotion. These are the slight movements animals make as they prepare to move, just as a person leans back and turns slightly when someone suddenly holds a fist up to his face. Relevant actions in birds include intention movements to fly and peck (Fig. 5–6). Gill-cover erection, an event associated with increased ventilation of the gills, is often seen in fish displays (Fig. 5–7), while many mammalian facial expressions may have originated from protective responses involving withdrawing the lips, lowering the eyebrows or flattening the ears (Fig. 5–4). Movements such as feather and hair erection for regulating body temperature, are also incorporated into bird and mammlian displays: witness the importance of crest or body feather erection in birds (Figs. 1–2; 5–6), and hair erection in dogs and cats (Fig. 5–8).

The assumption is that these events occurred in social situations for other reasons. For instance, high arousal could result in the need for cooling (hence feather erection), or increased ventilation (hence gill-cover erection). The need to escape injury would produce intention movements or protective responses. Through being associated with social events these actions would take on a signal value, enabling the recipient to

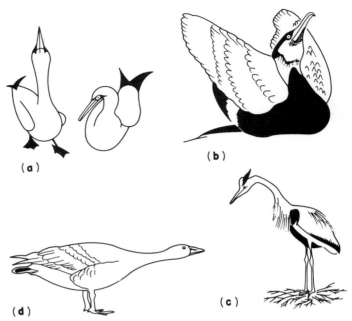

Fig. 5–6 Displays derived from intention movements to fly (**a** and **b**) and peck (**c** and **d**). (**a**) Sky-pointing in the gannet (*Sula bassana*) is given prior to leaving the nest. Note the stretching of the head and neck and the lifting of the wings. Sky-pointing helps coordinate nest relief; one partner never leaves while the other is still displaying. (From NELSON, J. B. (1965). *Brit. Birds*, **58**, 313–36.) (**b**) Wing-waving in the cormorant (*Phalacrocorax carbo*) is given near the male's nest site to attract a female. By repeatedly raising and lowering his wings the white rump patch is flashed twice a second. (**c**) The arch-neck upright display of the grey heron (*Ardea cinerea*) is used, mainly by the male, to defend his nest site in the colony. The plumes are raised and the bill pointed down and towards the opponent. (**d**) The forward posture of the greylag goose (*Anser anser*) is used to threaten other birds. (**b–d**) after CRAMP, S. and SIMMONS, K. E. L. (Eds) (1977). *The Birds of the Western Palearctic*, Vol. 1. Oxford University Press, Oxford.)

predict the behaviour of its partner and the signaller to eventually indicate its intentions. Subsequent evolution would result in *ritualization*; a specialization for communication by an improvement of efficiency. Movements become exaggerated, simplified, repeated rhythmically, and often associated with brightly coloured or conspicuous anatomical features. Signals of contrasting meaning, have evolved contrasting forms to minimize ambiguity – the principle of 'antithesis' (Fig. 5–8). Because of evolutionary changes, the origins of many signals can be obscure and only understood by comparing the behaviour seen in different contexts and in closely related species.

Conflict behaviour   The picture presented so far is incomplete for, while we have suggested the origin of some signals, we have not accounted for the complex patterning and meshing of these together to form displays, nor for the fact that different signals are often paired in different combinations. When a bird (such as a male great tit) disputes with a neighbour at a territorial boundary, it tends to attack on its own ground and flee when on its neighbour's. We therefore say that it has a *tendency* to attack or a tendency to flee according to the circumstances. At the territorial boundary, the bird is in a position where either behaviour is likely and in this situation the great tit shows its threat postures. The form of these postures is variable, each posture being associated with different probabilities of attacking and fleeing (Table 5). From evidence of this sort it is deduced that there is a *conflict* between the two opposing tendencies (to flee or attack), and that the behaviour shown reflects the balance of these tendencies. The same arguments can be applied to displays in other species and situations (Fig. 5–9). For example, many courtship displays seem to involve an interaction between the tendencies to approach, to flee and to behave sexually with the partner. It is clear, however, that this

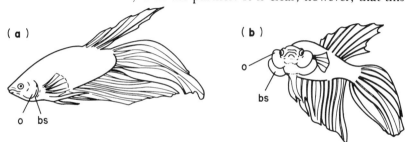

Fig. 5–7   Male Siamese fighting fish (*Betta splendens*). (a) Non-displaying. (b) Displaying. During the aggressive display the fins are erected and, as the opercula (gill covers) are raised, the black branchiostegal membranes (the opercular valves) protrude. (o, operculum; bs, branchiostegal membrane.) (After SIMPSON. M. J. A. (1968). *Animal Behaviour Monographs*, **1**, 1–73.)

Fig. 5–8   The principle of antithesis. The signals used in the aggressive posture of the dog (left) are reversed when it adopts a 'friendly' posture (right). (From DARWIN, C. (1872). *The Expression of Emotions in Man and Animals*. Murray, London.)

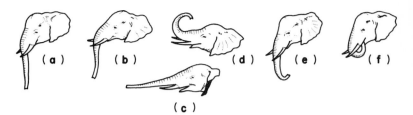

Fig. 5–9 The use of the head, trunk and ears in communication by African elephants. Note how the angle of the head and the position of the trunk and ears change with the mood of the animal. (a) Neutral position. (b) In a 'tense' mood. (c) Highly aggressive. (d) Slightly inhibited aggression. (e) Fearful but defensive. (f) Very fearful. There are many intermediate postures between those shown. (After KUHME, W. (1963). *Z. Tierpsychol.*, **20**, 66–79.)

theory cannot account *directly* for all display components. Intention movements to attack, flee or copulate obviously fit, but elements such as gill-cover erection or feather erection probably owe their origin (as outlined earlier), to the physiological consequences of vigorous activity and to the raised autonomic activity associated with conflict situations.

During conflict situations behaviour which seems irrelevant to both the situation and the tendencies in conflict is frequently seen. For example, threatening herring gulls peck and pull at grass, courting great-crested grebes and mallards make preening movements (Fig. 1–2), while a male stickleback may interrupt his courtship with swimming through his nest, a behaviour normally associated with fertilizing the eggs. The behaviour in these cases is usually incomplete and hurried. These so-called *displacement activities* occur when the animal's flow of behaviour is interrupted by a conflict between acting in incompatible ways, or if an animal is thwarted by, for example, a glass plate covering its food. Our interest in displacement activities in this chapter is that they provide another source of signals. After their incidental appearance in conflict situations, some have taken on a signal function and have been ritualized during the course of evolution. Displacement preening in ducks is very perfunctory. The wing is barely touched with the bill and the movement now serves to emphasize the colourful species-specific wing patches. For a more detailed discussion of conflict behaviour see MANNING (1979).

5.3.2   Selection pressures limiting signal evolution

Although many displays do involve conspicuous signals, it is clear that environmental factors limit signal evolution. A display is inevitably a compromise. Bright colours and loud calls may be useful in attracting mates but they will make the displayer more noticeable to predators. As a result, an equilibrium is established by natural selection, advantages and disadvantages being balanced. The equilibrium may not be the same for both sexes (female birds are often duller than males) or in different contexts (in some situations a caller can be located easily; in others this is not the case, Fig. 5–10). Another example is provided by nocturnal animals which emphasize olfactory and not visual signals.

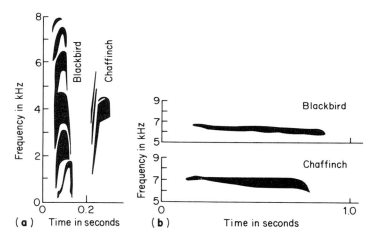

Fig. 5–10   Calls given by blackbirds and chaffinches when mobbing an owl (a) and 'warning' calls given in response to a hawk flying over (b). A mobbing bird is easy to locate because its calls are repeated in a rapid series and have a wide range of frequencies. By contrast a warning call is difficult to locate. Its pure tone, which fades in and out, gives the two ears less chance of picking up differences in intensity and time and so of using these features to locate the sound source. (After MARLER, P. (1959). *Darwin's Biological Work*, P. Bell (Ed.). Cambridge University Press, Cambridge, 150–206.)

6 The Dynamics of Social Interaction in Societies of Mammals and Birds

6.1 Describing intragroup behaviour

An important part of our description of social organization is a knowledge of how animals interact within their society. When we look at a society we soon notice that against the background of moving, feeding and resting, pulses of carefully structured social interaction occur as the animals communicate with each other. Even when not communicating they are usually aware of each other's behaviour and adjust their activities accordingly. When faced with the problem of trying to sort out what is going on, it is best to commence with general observations. Assuming that an ethogram (p. 4) has been drawn up and that age–sex classes (and if possible individuals) can be recognized, a start should be made by simply watching the flow of behaviour between animals. The animals which are involved in a social interaction and the behaviour they give to each other should be written down. With experience the observer becomes more perceptive and will want to reject his first attempts. A general picture will be built up of intragroup behaviour in terms of 'who does what to whom'. This is a sound way to start but soon *quantitative* methods may be necessary to answer specific research questions (p. 4). Since the flow of behaviour between individuals is inevitably overwhelming, it must be sampled and summarized.

Behaviour profiles An individual's social position has customarily been defined by reference to one or two variables (e.g. sex and rank), but this is now accepted as simplistic and a broader approach is adopted. Each individual's participation in numerous different types of behaviour must be considered. The relative importance and *interdependence* of different types of behaviour and individual relationships can then be assessed. Primatologists have made most progress in this direction. One technique is to construct *behaviour profiles* summarizing each individual's contribution to the group behaviour (Fig. 6–1). Individuals can be compared at a glance. One limitation is that behaviour profiles say nothing about social interactions and (once there are more than two animals in the group) nothing about *relationships* between individuals.

Interaction matrices To summarize interactions (and hence relationships) we use an *interaction matrix* (Fig. 6–2). Each matrix cell records the frequency with which a pair interact. A matrix usually refers to one behaviour such as playing, grooming or pecking. It can also summarize the *overall relative sociability* of individuals by recording all social interactions or exchanges of signals. One can similarly record the

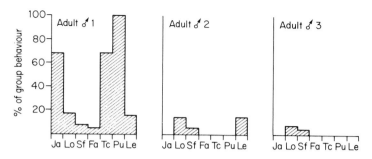

Fig. 6–1 The contrasting behaviour profiles of the three adult males in a group of vervet monkeys (*Cercopithecus aethiops*). Behaviour categories: territorial display – jumping around (Ja); social vigilance – looking out (Lo); social focus – the object of friendly approaches, not including the behaviour of mothers to their own infants (Sf); making friendly approaches (Fa); territorial chasing – the chasing out and exclusion of intruders from the group's territory (Tc); punishing – interferring in intragroup aggression (Pu); leading – the initiation of compact group movements (Le). (After GARTLAN, J. S. (1968). *Folia Primatol.*, **8**, 89–120.)

		Received pecks								Total pecks given	Hierarchy
	A	B	C	D	E	F	G	H	I		
A		152	97	38	26	23	15	43	21	415	A
B			103	76	22	27	34	17	18	297	B
C				23	29	29	58	18	78	235	C
D					23	11	41	14	17	106	D
E						32	21	11	0	64	E
F							18	27	0	45	F
G								13	28	41	G
H									31	31	H
I					41	22				63	I
	0	152	200	137	141	144	187	143	193	1297	

Gave pecks ↕ ; Total pecks received (bottom row)

Fig. 6–2 The distribution of pecks in a caged group of nine red jungle-fowl hens (*Gallus gallus*). This bird is considered, by some, to be ancestral to the domestic chicken (*G. domesticus*). Their behaviour is similar. Note the deviations from linearity due to bird (I). From BANKS, E. A. (1956). *Ecology*, **37**, 239–48.)

spatial arrangement of individuals by noting, for example, who perches next to whom. If all animals have had an *equal opportunity* to contribute to the table, then the row and column totals provide a useful summary of each animal's behaviour (Fig. 6–2). A correction must always be applied if the animals have been sampled unequally. One limitation of these matrices is that social behaviour is reduced to interactions between pairs – A simultaneously directing its behaviour to B *and* C, cannot be scored.

Sociograms A handy, diagrammatic way to portray relationships is the *sociogram* (Fig. 6–6). These are especially useful when large matrices contain so much information that major relationships are concealed. The sociogram in Fig. 6–6 shows what proportion of each animal's behaviour (in this case grooming) is *given to* each partner. Note, however, that in many cases it is equally important to know what proportion of the behaviour each animal receives, is *received from* each partner. For instance, one animal could direct all its threats to another, but these could quite easily represent a small proportion of the threats the latter receives. An instance of this is shown in Fig. 6–2 by animals H and I; $31/31 = 100\%$, but $31/193 =$ only 16%. From our knowledge of the interactions between group members and the pattern of relationships that exist between them, we build up a picture of the *social structure* of the group.

Age–sex class styles of behaviour and social roles We have so far emphasized the importance of measuring *individual* behaviour, since this is clearly the basis of social organization. It is essential, however, to compare the behaviour of individuals in a group (and also those in different groups) to see whether any valid *generalizations* can be made. For instance, are there sets of individuals who behave in a similar way? We can expect most divisions to be by age and sex; juvenile males may behave in one way, adult females in another. In some societies we find sets of individuals more closely defined than by age–sex class. The behaviour of high-ranking and low-ranking adult males may be characteristic and distinguishable, as may be that of lactating and childless adult females. Significantly, these positions or norms of behaviour seem to be a property of the society rather than of any particular individual. They occur repeatedly in different societies and if, for example, one removes the top male in a monkey group, another usually assumes his place and behaves in a similar way. For this and other reasons these social positions have been called *roles*, a term borrowed, somewhat uncritically, from sociology. Compare the roles of the adult male vervet monkeys in Fig. 6–1.

Individual variability These ways of describing animal social structure are in their infancy. Getting to grips with individual variability is difficult when individuals can vary in so many ways. The problem is often ignored but that does not make it less pressing. Zoologists are traditionally reluctant to refer seriously to differences in temperament and personality in animals and yet concepts like these may be essential, especially in primates. It should now be appreciated why it is so essential to score the behaviour of *individuals*. Lumping together all the individuals in an age–sex class might well conceal important individual differences. If behaviour is considered at the age–sex class level, always correct for any unevenness of numbers in the classes. For more examples of how to analyse the behaviour of animals in groups see HINDE (1974).

6.2   Sampling methods

How do we set about collecting data to use in the above ways? Obviously this depends on the precise question being asked, but the universal principle is to develop *unbiased sampling methods*. By paying insufficient attention to this, biased data will be obtained because the observer will spend more time watching animals doing interesting or unusual things, or those animals which are easiest to see. All relevant individuals must be equally sampled, for example, by watching each for a fixed period of time. If this is impractical then the duration of the sample must be recorded and a correction subsequently applied to allow for unequal sampling. It must be ensured that all individuals are observed at equivalent times of the day.

The most reliable and widely used sampling methods are *focal animal sampling* and *instantaneous sampling*. In focal sampling, attention is focused for a specified period of time on each animal in turn and its flow of behaviour recorded. The results can be used to estimate the percentage of time engaged in each activity, the rates of behavioural events and their duration. With instantaneous sampling a target animal is chosen and its behavioural state is recorded at pre-set intervals (e.g. every 5 or 30 s). The percentage of time devoted to each behaviour can be calculated. It is sometimes necessary to scan across a whole group of animals and the method is then called *scan sampling*. These samples give additional information on the synchrony of behaviour between individuals. Focal animal and instantaneous sampling suffer from the disadvantage of not recording the structure of social interactions. If this is required another method, *sequence* or *interaction sampling* is available. It relies on the observer focusing his attention on social interactions rather than particular individuals. Details are recorded of the individuals joining and leaving the interaction and of the flow of behaviour between them. The method may be applied to specific sorts of interaction (e.g. grooming) or more generally. Bias may creep in when the observer is deciding which interactions to record. A summary of sampling methods is provided by ALTMANN (1974).

6.3   The types of social behaviour seen in societies

Before discussing two cases in detail (see §§ 6.4 and 6.5), the rich variety of social behaviour found in mammal and bird societies must be mentioned. *Agonistic behaviour* is seen in most species: it includes *aggression* (the behaviour of attack and threat), *flight* from an opponent and *submission*. The latter covers avoidance, crouching and signals that indicate acceptance of another's superiority. The context of agonistic behaviour is very variable. For example, monkeys may compete for food, water, sexual partners, resting positions, grooming or other social partners. *Courtship* functions in mate selection, sexual isolation and to synchronize the behaviour and physiology of sexual partners. *Sexual behaviour* is of obvious importance but remember that in multi-male societies it only provides an indirect and approximate measure of a male's reproductive success (p. 22). *Social preening* and *grooming* are often seen in courtship displays and in many other situations (p. 64).

Animals reuniting after separation often give a *greeting* display. These are particularly common in birds rejoining their mate at the nest: as a white stork (*Ciconia ciconia*) lands the pair vigorously clatter their bills and bend their heads right back. Under similar circumstances one gannet may rattle its bill against its mate's. Such signals indicate mutual recognition and the signaller's non-aggressive intent (Fig. 5–2).

The selective advantage of *parental care* cannot be over-emphasized – witness the number of species showing this in one form or another and the energy devoted to it. Parental care is obviously most important when young are born in a relatively helpless state, as in most mammals and birds. *Maternal care* is pre-eminent but *paternal care* occurs when a male can increase his offsprings' survival by helping his mate (p. 81). Male birds can easily feed their new young but a male mammal cannot and paternal care is less frequent. *Vigilance* against predators aids survival and when a male stays with his female and offspring he usually plays a key role in this activity. For instance when spotted hyaenas chase a zebra group the single stallion drops back snapping and kicking at the predators. When groups of kin stay together, *aid-giving behaviour* is found, siblings helping each other and their parents.

Interesting *cooperative* behaviour is seen in the social carnivores, the lions, hunting dogs, hyaenas and wolves. Most solitary carnivores hunt prey smaller than themselves but cooperative hunting makes these beasts formidable killers. We know little of how cooperative hunting is controlled and *leadership* in general proves a difficult problem to handle. One cannot assume that the animal at the front of the group is the leader: animals like generals may lead from the rear. The direction of travel is often a compromise between the behaviour of several animals. In sacred baboons (p. 86) two harems may move about together in a coordinated manner. One of the adult males, usually the younger, initiates movements but the group does not proceed unless the other, elder male concurs.

Finally, species with a marked juvenile period often show considerable *play* during which motor and social skills are developed. The development of social behaviour presents some exciting problems which are introduced in the next chapter.

6.4   Aggression and submission

6.4.1   Domestic chickens

It is common to single out one animal in a society as the dominant animal or 'top dog'. To consider what is behind such a label we can start with a familiar example, the agonistic behaviour of the domestic chicken. In one experiment, individually colour-marked day-old chicks were put into groups of about 20 and their behavioural development studied for 21 weeks. Pecks between chicks and peck-like aggressive approaches (considered to be threats) were scored. Pecks appeared late in the second week (when they were rare) and subsequently increased in frequency. Avoidance of aggressive actions appeared in the fifth week. After the sixth week the chicks could be sexed and a look back through the results revealed behavioural differences between the sexes. Males were much more aggressive than females (Table 6). In adults, males peck males and females peck females, but heterosexual pecking is rare; this pattern emerged as the chicks aged (Fig. 6–3). At first, pecking and avoidance were not distributed in a regular pattern between individuals. During weeks 6 to 13 the behaviour of each like-sexed pair became predictable, one pecking the other which retreated or avoided its aggressor. We therefore say that a *dominant–subordinate relationship* was established between the pair. Individual recognition had presumably developed by this time, or alternatively the birds learnt the general characteristics of birds they could and could not dominate. These relationships are basically *hierarchical* in form, each bird pecking those below it in the hierarchy (Fig. 6–2) and avoiding those above it, but there are exceptions. In the mixed

Table 6   Sex differences in aggression in chicks 2–6 weeks old. Scores represent the number of pecks and peck-like aggressive approaches given during the observation period. The group contained ten males (σ) and eight females ($\female$). The numbers in brackets give the scores that would be expected if there were no sex differences, making allowance for the uneven sex ratio. (Data from GUHL, A. M. (1958). *Anim. Behav.*, 6, 92–111.)

	Peck-like action	Pecks	Total
σ pecks σ	46 (17.7)	16 (8.2)	62 (25.9)
σ pecks $\female$	12 (15.7)	9 (7.3)	21 (23.0)
$\female$ pecks σ	2 (15.7)	2 (7.3)	4 (23.0)
$\female$ pecks $\female$	0 (11.0)	1 (5.1)	1 (16.1)
Totals	60 (60.1)	28 (27.9)	88 (88.0)

flocks the low frequency of pecking between the sexes meant that two hierarchies (peck-orders) emerged; the males' at 11 weeks and the females' at 13 weeks.

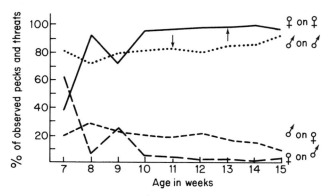

Fig. 6–3 The emergence of unisexual pecking in a flock of 18 domestic chicks (8♀, 10♂). The arrows indicate the time at which the male and female peck-orders were formed. Based on 3585 pecks by the males, 625 by the females. (From GUHL, A.M. (1958).*Anim. Behav.*, **6**, 92–111.)

Some definitions The animal at the top of a hierarchy is often referred to as the *dominant* or α animal. But note that the terms 'dominant' and 'subordinate' strictly refer to the relationship between a *pair* of animals. It is better to use the terms *high-ranking, highest ranking, low-ranking*, etc., when referring to the *position* of an animal in a hierarchy. It will be noticed that the term *dominance hierarchy* has been avoided. This is quite intentional since it incorrectly implies that a hierarchy is based solely on aggression. A hierarchy does not exist as a distinct entity; it is simply a consequence of the dominant–subordinate relationships of pairs of individuals. These are based on aggression *and* submission, and it is therefore more accurate to speak of an *agonistic hierarchy*. Chickens avoid facing dominant birds and readily indicate their subordinate status by fleeing. On the other hand, a bird may face its subordinates and may move threateningly towards them with the neck outstretched and neck feathers extended. Many confrontations are resolved without fighting, and submission perpetuates rank relationships. Further information on the social behaviour of chickens is provided by WOOD-GUSH (1971).

6.4.2 Baboons and macaques

Dyadic agonistic interactions Some of the most detailed studies of agonistic behaviour have been made on ground-dwelling monkeys such as baboons and macaques. If a feeding group is watched, it will be noticed that the animals tend to maintain a minimum distance (the so-called *individual distance*) from their neighbours. Some animals avoid others by simply moving out of their way but, of course, some instances are more complex, one monkey having threatened or attacked the other. Most will be *dyadic* interactions, involving just two animals. Whatever the species being studied it is best to start by examining these interactions if we are interested in the agonistic relationships between individuals. Separate matrices are drawn up to summarize the distribution between individuals of dyadic avoidance, threats and attacks. The matrices indicate how consistent the behaviour is, whether a hierarchical pattern of relationships exists and if so whether it is linear. Examination of the row and column totals reveals how much of these different types of agonistic behaviour each individual gives and receives.

Details of the distribution of submission between individuals are rarely recorded. And yet, when equal emphasis was placed on recording aggression and submission in captive common baboons, submissive behaviour appeared to be even more important than aggression in maintaining the dominant–subordinate relationship. The importance of submission has clearly been underestimated in other species. In Barbary macaques it was found that aggression and submission played a more even role, the precise balance of the two depending on the position of the animals in the hierarchy. Dominant–subordinate relationships are *dynamic* and each confrontation can be considered a learning situation, reinforcing or tending to change existing relationships. Caution should be exercised in equating dominance and aggressiveness, for these are not synonyms: dominance refers to a relationship, aggressiveness to the tendency to attack or threaten. Animals lower down a hierarchy may in fact be more aggressive than those at the top.

More complex agonistic interactions A most interesting fact emerging from studies of baboons and macaques, is the importance of agonistic interactions involving more than two participants. Under these circumstances the interactants' behaviour may be changed considerably, even producing reversals in relationships and hence the hierarchy. Macaques and baboons exploit *protected threat*. Two animals may be threatening and lunging towards each other when one backs away towards a high-ranking animal and presents, sits near or grooms it. From this secure position threatening may be continued. Any threat the opponent makes is also received by the high-ranking animal who may intervene (Fig. 6–4). Infants and juveniles frequently use adult males in this way. *Mutual support* also figures prominently and may be specifically solicited (p. 42). One monkey sides with another in threatening and chasing opponents who may rank higher than one or both of them. Siblings often support each other and the behaviour is also seen among adult males. In one recorded case a young adult male common baboon, A, allied with an old male, B. Acting together at the top of the hierarchy,

Fig. 6–4 'Protected threat' in sacred baboons. The female (centre) presents to the male (left) while threatening another animal (right). (From WICKLER, W. (1967). In: *Primate Ethology*, D. Morris (Ed.). Weidenfeld and Nicolson, London.)

they outranked another male, C, who individually ranked higher than A. B later disappeared and A, now without his support, dropped below C. It is commoner to observe maternal intervention in support of offspring. The breaking up of fights by threatening or chasing the participants, is often done by high-ranking adult males and females.

We have little information on how protected threat develops. Does each individual learn from experience? Does a young monkey learn that looking at its mother during a fight provokes her intervention? Our ignorance of these issues is profound. Protected threat is an example of the exciting phenomenon of *social buffering* in which one individual makes use of another to regulate its relations with a third party. Male Barbary macaques frequently carry babies and use them as a 'passport' to social interaction with other males. Otherwise-unapproachable high-ranking males are approached if they, or the approacher, are in possession of a baby (Fig. 6–5). This form of social buffering in which a baby is used to regulate another's agonistic behaviour is called *agonistic buffering*. This is also seen in other species but interestingly, each case is somewhat different. Male common baboons may carry an infant to enhance their rank when challenging another male, while sub-adult male sacred baboons may hold or carry an infant during a fight and so appease an adult male aggressor.

Kinship and rank   In most primates, adult males outrank adult females

(a)   (b)   (c)

Fig. 6–5   Barbary macaque monkeys. In a characteristic social interaction a sub-adult male uses a baby to get close to an adult male. After presenting the baby to him (a) and (b), the sub-adult is able to sit close to the adult and groom him (c). (Drawn from photographs by the author.)

but it has taken long-term studies of Japanese and rhesus macaques to reveal details of rank determination. Sex, age and physique are important but a fundamental factor is maternal rank. In these matrilineal societies (p. 22) the principle of *young ascendancy* operates: as young females mature they take up a hierarchical position below their mother and above their older sisters. Genealogies therefore, rank below each other in descending order of their matriarch's rank. Undoubtedly the major factor operating is maternal support and mutual support by siblings. An animal's rank assessed by dyadic agonistic behaviour, without the influence of any other monkey, is called its *basic rank*. If in the presence of a third monkey, an animal's rank relative to another changes, then this is its *dependent rank*. Maternal and sibling support are obviously important determinants of dependent rank and as an animal matures their effect may be assimilated into its basic rank.

The problem of defining rank   Up to this point a problem that has dogged students of social behaviour (particularly primatologists) for decades has been avoided. The problem is how to define rank – an issue still current today. In the 1920s when T. Schjelderup-Ebbe introduced the idea of peck-orders in birds, he defined rank with reference to agonistic behaviour. Very different criteria were soon added by primatologists. Rank has been measured by agonistic behaviour (usually aggression), sexual behaviour, grooming, non-sexual mounting and by priority in gaining food and water and in avoiding electric shocks. These different criteria would not matter if there was a good correlation between them, but this is not always the case. For example, the α male is not always the most sexually active and the relationship between rank and grooming is complex because of the latter's variable motivation (see § 6.5). The most useful method is to define rank initially by reference to the distribution of dyadic aggression and submission. Other behaviour can then be assessed separately and related where appropriate to rank. If this approach is adopted it becomes useful to distinguish between rank and *status*. The latter is a broader-based description of an animal's position in the group including, for example, rank, leadership, grooming, sexual behaviour and priority to food. For an extended discussion of the agonistic behaviour of primates see HINDE (1974) or ROWELL (1972).

Interspecific differences in behaviour   This discussion should not be terminated without noting important interspecific differences in primate agonistic behaviour. In some species, particularly forest monkeys and even some forest populations of baboons, agonistic behaviour is infrequent and it is unreasonable to describe their relationships as hierarchical. In contrast, captive groups of most species have clear hierarchies and this may be the result of an unnatural group structure and environment. For species that live in small family groups the whole concept of hierarchical relationships may be unhelpful and inappropriate. An extreme opinion is that hierarchies are absent or tenuous in wild primates. This is incorrect, but we must certainly be cautious about results from captive animals or wild populations which are artificially fed.

6.5   Social grooming

As a contrasting example to agonistic behaviour, social grooming and social preening will be considered. Most animals groom themselves by one means or another to remove parasites, other sources of irritation and to recondition their pellage. Social grooming (often called *allogrooming*), in which one animal grooms another, is less widespread and is seen primarily in birds and mammals. To some extent social grooming has a cleansing function. In New Forest ponies (*Equus caballus*) mutual social grooming (i.e. two animals simultaneously grooming each other) is a response to irritation by lice and shedding hair. Two ponies stand facing each other and nibble at each others' neck, mane and back and other parts which a pony finds it difficult to reach itself. In a similar way, birds tend to concentrate on the head and throat, and Japanese monkeys on the back, flanks and crown of the head.

Social grooming has important social functions. Its motivation may be quite varied and we must not simply label it an amicable activity. This is certainly not so in mice and rats which allogroom with their teeth, tongue and paws. The behaviour is often associated with the groomer behaving aggressively to a crouching and submissive partner. A similar situation exists in birds, where aggressive pecking by one bird may give way to it preening the partner. Social preening often occurs between mates who of necessity must be in close proximity at the nest site (e.g. gannets and kittiwakes). It seems that allopreening occurs when the aggressive behaviour of one bird is thwarted by its partner refusing to flee. The preened bird often adopts a submissive-like posture turning its bill away from the preener. Parents may also preen their young.

6.5.1   *Social grooming in primates*

The most detailed studies of social grooming have been made on the primates whose hands obviously lend themselves to this activity. The information given here is drawn mainly from macaques and baboons. The groomer slides the fur aside with one hand while scraping and picking through it with the other. Particles are removed with the fingers or the mouth. The most intense and relaxed grooming sessions (the groomee often sitting with eyes closed and body limp), take place near the sleeping site, or around midday if the animals can take time off from feeding. Details of the initiation of a grooming bout depend on the context (see below). One animal may simply approach the other, sit down beside it and start to groom. Alternatively, the groomee may actively solicit grooming by laying down in front of the other monkey and tilting the head or body towards it. The groomee may control the parts groomed by changing position or lifting a limb and so offering a new surface to the groomer.

Two ways of discovering the significance of social grooming are to examine its distribution between group members and to record the context in which it occurs.

Grooming and kinship   Although most individuals groom at one time or another, most activity centres around adult females with young. In one rhesus monkey group 62% of the grooming took place between matrilineal kin. There were 38 monkeys in the group and hence $38 \times 37 = 1406$ possible grooming partners, 212 (15%) of which involved matrilineal kin. Some relatives were not observed to groom and so less than 15% of the group accounted for 62% of the grooming. Much of the grooming within genealogies can be classified as *relaxed social grooming*. During periods of inactivity the relatives settle down in small grooming parties and grooming continues for minutes at a time. Grooming partners frequently change, each animal playing the roles of groomer and groomee. Mothers groom their young, but this wanes as the young mature and start to associate more with their siblings. A mother receives a greater proportion of her offspring's grooming than they receive of hers (Fig. 6–6). We may think of relaxed social grooming as strengthening and maintaining close social relationships that already exist.

Exploiting the pleasurable nature of receiving grooming   The fact that animals solicit grooming, compete for a groomer's attention, and the relaxed postures groomees adopt, all indicate that being groomed is a pleasant experience. It is perhaps, therefore, not surprising that the pleasurable nature of receiving grooming is exploited in many situations. This is the case when one animal uses social grooming to enable it to stay in another's company and so obtain a goal. Such grooming is usually not reciprocated. Adolescent female rhesus macaques groom mothers to keep close to them and gradually shift their attention to the mothers' infants. Males may also use grooming to keep close to high-ranking males (Fig. 6–5). Adult males rarely groom adult females unless they are consorting with them: grooming is then used to maintain the reduced individual distance necessary for the temporary courtship bond.

Grooming also occurs in a variety of *agonistic situations* but it seems that the aggressive grooming of birds and rodents has little or no primate counterpart. In primates the groomer is usually the subordinate and the grooming is rarely reciprocated. Grooming may be used to form a temporary bond with a high-ranking animal or to appease an aggressor while lowering fear in the groomer. A monkey that has been threatened may approach a high-ranking male and groom it. Such behaviour is closely related to the protected threat sequences discussed above. Alternatively, the threatened monkey may approach its threatener and groom it in a hurried and exaggerated fashion. Another monkey may

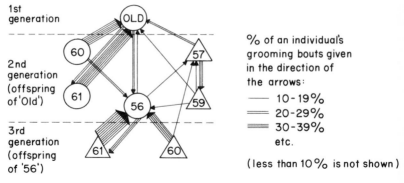

Fig. 6–6   The distribution of grooming within a matrilineal genealogy of rhesus monkeys. Circles represent females; triangles, males. Monkey 'Old' was the founding female, the other animals' numbers refer to their year of birth (e.g. '59' was born in 1959). (After HANBY, J. P. (1974). *Symp. 5th Cong. International Primat. Soc.*, 25–42, using information from D. S. Sade.)

even intervene in a fight and solicit grooming from either participant and so terminate the aggression. It is this variation in context and motivation that makes primate social grooming such a fascinating topic. It also explains why, although grooming is generally directed to higher-ranked animals, any correlations with rank are by no means perfect.

7 Social Development

7.1 The interaction of factors in development

Offhand remarks linking someone's unconventional social behaviour with early events in life are common. The endless clichés involve dominant mothers, deprived childhoods, poor starts to life and traits that 'run in the family'. The precise significance of such factors in the complex process of human development can, of course, be difficult to establish. The purpose of this chapter is not, however, to pursue this point but instead to illustrate the problems from a biological point of view, by examining the factors that influence the development of animal social behaviour. The influence of one animal on the social development of another will be emphasized, but we must also consider other aspects of the developing organisms' environment including, somewhat surprisingly, even its own behaviour.

7.1.1 Interaction between genes and the environment

Each animal has instructions for behavioural development coded in its genes, but these do not control development independently. The behaviour produced is the result of an interaction between the inherited instructions and the developing organism's environment. In the case of social behaviour, examples of relevant environmental influences are population density, aggressive behaviour received, maternal social rank, the opportunity to practice behaviour during play, and so on.

7.1.2 Investigating environmental effects

Deprivation experiments are commonly used to study the relative importance of inheritance and environment in social development. Animals are deprived of an environmental factor (e.g. isolated without their mother or other social partner) and their development compared with a control group of undeprived animals. It is important to appreciate the limitations of this experimental design. Any differences in development between the deprived and control groups may be attributable to the differences in their environment, for example the opportunity of one animal to learn from another. On the other hand, if a behaviour develops correctly under deprivation conditions, we *cannot* conclude that the behaviour is determined solely by the genes; other aspects of the environment are still present including the possibility of the animal practising by interacting with itself (see p. 69).

A similar point was made earlier (p. 10), when it was emphasized that the environment must be adequately controlled before conclusions can be drawn about the genetic basis of any differences in behaviour between animals of different strains. While it is difficult to specify the precise importance of inheritance for most behaviours, it is easier to demonstrate that aspects of the environment are important. An example in the caste determination of female honeybees has already been given (p. 34). Differential feeding is involved, but it clearly only works because the larvae have an inherited ability to respond to differences in diet.

7.1.3   Genes, physiology and experience

In addition to this fundamental interaction between inheritance and experience, social development also involves interaction between genetic and physiological systems within the animal. Changes in social behaviour may, for example, be linked with post-natal growth of the nervous system or hormonal changes. Changes in these may, of course, be themselves linked with environmental experience. This can be illustrated by the development of non-human primate sexual behaviour. At the chromosomal level, sex is determined by the sex chromosomes, a female being XX and a male XY. A gene or genes on the Y chromosome confers maleness to the embryo and results in differentiation away from the basic female form. Testes develop (in contrast to ovaries), a male pattern of hormone secretion is established (non-cyclical in contrast to cyclical), as does a male pattern of responsiveness in the brain to circulating hormones (see SLATER, 1978). The secondary sexual characteristics develop later. Behavioural differences are established early; young male common baboons and macaques play more boisterously and spend less time near their mothers than young females do. This sex difference is due both to their physiological maleness and to the fact that mothers treat males differently from females. The development of adequate sexual behaviour in monkeys depends on social experience. Socially deprived males assume incorrect postures and respond inappropriately to social gestures (Fig. 7–1). A more subtle result of experience is seen in nature; rhesus males tend not to mate with their mothers.

7.2   The development of a social signal

Chaffinch song   In spring and early summer the adult male chaffinch repeatedly sings from prominent positions as it establishes its territory. The song, which signals territory ownership to male intruders and attracts unpaired females, has three descending phrases and a terminal flourish (Fig. 7–2a). It lasts for 2–2.5 s and is repeated at regular intervals of between 7 and 15 s. Each male has a repertoire of up to six song types which it sings in various sequences. In its first summer a young bird gives a variety of fledgling calls. By late summer these develop into a subsong, differing from the full song in several respects. It is quieter, of irregular length and phase structure, has a wider range of notes and no terminal flourish (Fig. 7–2b). Subsong is a practice for the full song and has no

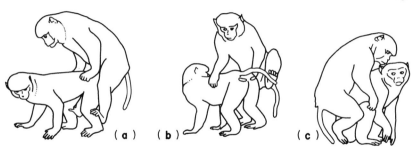

Fig. 7–1 Sexual behaviour of wild-born and socially deprived male rhesus monkeys with socially experienced females. (a) Wild-born male in typical copulatory position. (b and c) Inadequate sexual behaviour of males born in the laboratory and reared alone but allowed to see and hear other young monkeys. The key component of their deprivation is their lack of play with other infants. Females reared under similar conditions are also sexually inadequate and make poor mothers. (From MASON, W. A. (1965). In: *Primate Behaviour*, I. DeVore (Ed.). Holt, Rinehart and Winston, New York.)

obvious communicatory function. It ceases during the late autumn but resumes during the late winter, developing into the full song during the spring.

Experiments with chaffinch song development Experiments have revealed an interesting interaction between inheritance and experience in the development of the chaffinch song. Hand-reared birds and those caught in their first autumn were kept in auditory isolation or given different experience of hearing vocalizations. This affected the characteristics of their adult songs (Fig. 7–3). Birds hand-reared in auditory isolation gave the normal subsong but their adult song was simple. These simple songs cannot be referred to as innate components of the full song; the birds will have had experience of hearing themselves sing. Birds exposed to adult song in their first autumn (artificially or in the wild) sing near-normal adult songs, even if kept in isolation. It seems that the birds carry a

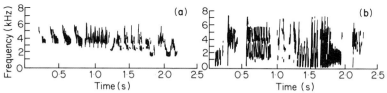

Fig. 7–2 (a) An example of the full song of an adult male chaffinch as displayed by a sound spectrograph machine which plots frequency against time. The standard mnemonic for the three phrases and terminal flourish is 'chip-chip-chip-chip', 'tell-tell-tell-tell', 'cherry-erry-erry-erry', 'tissy-che-wee-ooo'. (b) An example of chaffinch subsong. (From THORPE, W. H. (1961). *Bird-Song*. The University Press, Cambridge.)

memory of the song and modify their calls to match this. The importance of auditory feedback was further demonstrated by deafening birds at various stages of song development. Birds deafened when mature still sang their full songs for up to two to three years. Birds deafened at earlier ages did not develop full songs; their songs reflected the stage of vocal development reached before deafening.

Further evidence for the importance of learning is provided by group-rearing experiments, in which birds stimulated each other and adjusted their performance to match their companions' (Fig. 7–3). Even more convincing, are experiments in which isolated, hand-reared chaffinches were exposed to modified songs with, for example, a central flourish: they adopted the same song pattern. In nature the effect of social experience is shown by the presence of *song dialects*. Chaffinches living in an area share common song patterns, with differences occurring between birds in different localities. The ability to learn songs does not continue indefinitely. By about one year of age a bird is left with the song repertoire it has at that time. The termination of the sensitive period for learning, is associated with the rise in concentration of the sex hormone testosterone in the maturing male. Castration prolongs the sensitive period which may then be terminated by injecting testosterone.

REARING CONDITIONS						CHARACTERISTICS OF ADULT SONG
Wild birds	Caught in 1st autumn and kept:		Hand reared from five days old, isolated from normal song and kept:			
	in small groups with peers	as single birds in auditory isolation	as single birds in auditory isolation but exposed to recorded adult song	in small groups with peers	as single birds in auditory isolation	
					✓	Simple song, no phrases or terminal flourish
				✓*		Slightly more complex song with some phrases but no terminal flourish
		✓	✓			Nearly normal song
✓*	✓*					Normal song

Fig. 7–3 The characteristics of the songs produced by adult male chaffinches reared under different conditions. (*Each experimental group – or area in the case of wild birds – has a unique and distinctive song pattern because each bird modifies its song to match its companions'.) (Based on the results of THORPE, W. H. (1961). *Bird-Song*. The University Press, Cambridge.)

Other species   The relative importance of social learning in song development varies between species. The European cuckoo (*Cuculus canorus*) gives its own species' call and not its host's song: cuckoos reared in auditory isolation call normally. The same is true of many invertebrates, such as crickets, in which behaviour generally develops fully in the absence of the opportunity to learn from conspecifics. The short life-span and frequent lack of parental care make this adaptive.

7.3   The development of social relationships

The social relationship between two individuals in a society is defined by the characteristics of the social interactions between them (Chapter 6). Social relationships do not just appear: they develop, growing and waning according to the circumstances, as we know from our own lives. When there is a particularly enduring and positive (i.e. principally non-agonistic) relationship between two animals we talk of there being a *bond* between them. The most frequently discussed are the mother–offspring bond and the pair-bond.

7.3.1   Imprinting in birds

The development of the mother–offspring bond is particularly interesting in young birds such as ducklings, chicks and goslings that leave the nest shortly after hatching. Downy feathered, strong of leg and capable of feeding themselves, they must recognize their mother and follow her for protection and to find food. Soon after hatching, these young birds show a marked tendency to follow a conspicuous moving stimulus (the so-called 'following response') and to become attached to it. In nature the stimulus object is the mother (who calls as well) or siblings; in the laboratory young birds are far from discriminating in what they follow. Ducklings hatched in isolation will follow and form an attachment to a wide range of conspicuous, moving, visual stimuli: people, balloons and coloured blocks all work, but stimuli emitting maternal-like calls are particularly effective. The learning process resulting in the attachment is called *filial imprinting*. By hatching eggs in isolation and then exposing young of different ages to a stimulus and subsequently testing for discrimination, a sensitive period is found during which imprinting is most likely to occur. This is between 10–20 h after hatching in mallard ducks. The fact that imprinting is less likely after that time, means that in the wild the young are not distracted on to other stimuli. In fact, once imprinting has occurred the young birds flee from novel objects.

The immediate consequences of imprinting have been emphasized, but we must also note that, in some species, imprinting in the early weeks of life influences *adult* social behaviour. For instance, cross-fostering experiments reveal that male zebra finches and male mallards subsequently tend to court females of the species on which they were imprinted. The sensitive period for this process of *sexual imprinting* is generally longer (for mallard ducks it may last for several weeks), and the preferences established may last a lifetime. In nature, sexual imprinting reduces the chance of an individual mating with the wrong species.

7.3.2   Social development of monkeys

The mother–infant relationship   Monkeys make neither nests or dens for their relatively helpless newborn young and carry them wherever they go. Endowed with firmly gripping fingers and toes a baby clings to its mother's ventral surface even before it has the strength and coordination to stand on all-fours. As the mother sits the baby slumps in her lap, raising itself to suckle as necessary. When she rises she pulls the baby briefly to her ventrum and it responds by holding tight. Some weeks later it will start to ride on her back. From this relatively helpless state the baby's behaviour unfolds. It becomes more aware of the world, more independent of its mother and establishes relationships with siblings, peers and other group members. Most effort has been devoted towards understanding the development of the mother–infant relationship of rhesus monkeys, which can be kept in the laboratory in small groups of a male, two to four females and their young. As a baby grows it spends more and more time off its mother (Fig. 7–4a) and out of arm's reach. The mother plays the major role in maintaining mother–infant proximity during the first weeks (she is responsible for a higher proportion of approaches than leavings), but the situation is soon reversed. The infant subsequently plays the major role, being responsible for a higher proportion of approaches than leavings (Fig. 7–4b). Careful analysis has shown that, in spite of the fact that the infant is quickly maturing and interacting with an increasing number of animals, it is actually the *mother* who is largely responsible for the increasing time the infant spends off and at a distance from her. The infant is therefore playing a larger role in maintaining proximity (Fig. 7–4b) because the mother is playing a smaller one. Mothers also take less and less initiative in establishing nipple contact and infants attempting to get to the nipple are rejected more and more frequently during their first year of life. This changing relationship is influenced by several factors. The young monkey is maturing physically and becoming mobile as its limbs gain strength and its movements become more coordinated. At the same time its perceptual abilities develop and it becomes more aware of the world. It starts to take solid food and becomes nutritionally independent by six to eight months. The infant, however, still returns regularly to its mother and snuggles close to her ventrum. Occasional suckling, presumably non-nutritive, may continue until the next sibling is born.

The importance of play and care by siblings   Laboratory work places most emphasis on the mother–infant relationship. But in nature an infant

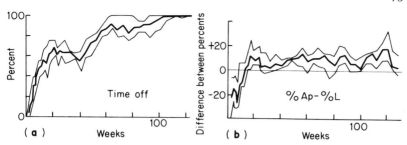

Fig. 7–4 Age changes in rhesus monkey mother–infant interaction. Medians and interquartile ranges for 16 infants (weeks 1–24) or 8 infants (weeks 24–130). (a) Number of ½-minute periods in which infant was off mother (as percentage of the number of ½-minute periods observed). (b) Infant initiative in maintaining proximity (percentage of approaches (Ap) due to infant, minus percentage of leavings (L) due to infant (% Ap – % L)). (From HINDE, R. A. and SPENCER-BOOTH, Y. (1971). *Science*, **173**, 111–18.)

develops within the social environment provided by the whole group and quickly starts to interact with other infants and its siblings. In macaques and baboons social play starts within the first few weeks of life. It seems obvious that play facilitates development of motor and social skills and there is some experimental evidence that this is so. Macaque females, principally childless adolescents persistently approach mothers with babies. They are frequently the baby's siblings and they sit with the mother, groom her and may eventually be rewarded for their persistence, by being allowed to groom and carry the baby. There are considerable interspecific differences in the mothers' permissiveness. Langur mothers (*Presbytis entellus*, Asiatic leaf-eating monkeys) allow females to handle and carry their young within hours of birth, but most macaques allow only touching and not carrying during the first few weeks of life. Mothers frequently sit together, their infants playing and periodically returning to them or their siblings. As described earlier, this close interaction between maternal kin influences many aspects of social development from rank to choice of grooming partners (see pp. 22 and 62). There is also a mutual interaction between the social development of siblings: care endowed by adolescent females on their young siblings gives them practice in maternal skills as well as benefiting the young.

7.4 Social development and social organization

Social control of sexual development   So far the emphasis has been on how one animal may influence another's social development, but it would sometimes be more appropriate to state that one animal *controls* the other's development. In the most fundamental cases sexual development and reproductive potential is controlled. Thus, the queen honeybee suppresses her workers' ovarian development (p. 34) and in wolf packs only one female may reproduce at a time, the others' sexual development being curtailed by fighting. An analogous case is seen in bumble bees, where the queen's aggressive behaviour stops the workers' ovaries developing. These examples illustrate the interdependence of social development and social organization.

Cyclical changes in social relationships   In seasonal breeders (e.g. great tits and red deer), cyclical changes in social relationships occur and play a major role in the dynamics of social organization. Switching to the territorial, reproductive social phase in great tits and black-headed gulls, depends (as shown on pp. 30 and 31) on the development of aggressive behaviour associated with territoriality and on the emergence of a pair-bond. Each bird's behaviour develops until tuned to that of its mate; aggression to the mate is suppressed as close cooperation develops. Any mismatch in behaviour may result in failure to mate or loss of young (Fig. 2–1). The development of such seasonal behaviour has a clear physiological basis (Fig. 7–5); physiological activity is in turn triggered by environmental factors such as daylength (see SLATER, 1978).

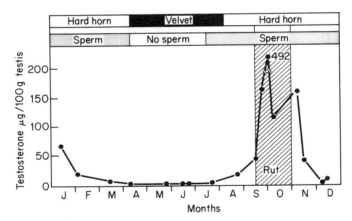

Fig. 7–5   The rutting season and seasonal changes in antler condition, spermatogenesis and testis testosterone in the red deer stag. Antlers are cast between mid-March and May. Rutting behaviour coincides with a marked increase in testosterone levels. (From LINCOLN, G . A. (1971). *J. Zool. Lond.*, **163**, 105–23.)

8 Why be Social?

8.1   Is social behaviour adaptive?

In earlier chapters it was stated that animals behave in this way or that because it is adaptive for them to do so. But what evidence do we require to be sure that this really is the case? Are other explanations sometimes possible? For instance, do some animals behave in an apparently maladaptive way, by not reproducing or by surrendering food to others, because this is forced upon them? This discussion of the adaptiveness of social behaviour will focus on individuals since the general applicability of population selection has been discounted (p. 18).

The adaptiveness of social behaviour sometimes seems to be so obvious that there appears to be nothing to discuss. This is often the case when behaviour which is characteristic of a species as a whole is examined. At this level the functions of some behaviour (e.g. maternal care, courtship displays) appear as obvious as the functions of fins and feathers. This is, however, a superficial approach which incorrectly implies that the behaviour is shown equally by all individuals. In fact some mothers give different care from others; some members of a population may be territorial and others not; some may not breed, and so on.

8.1.1   Investigating the adaptive significance of social behaviour

Two main attitudes are adopted when investigating the adaptive significance of social behaviour. In the first, the observer notes a behavioural situation (e.g. colonial nesting under some conditions and solitary nesting under others) and then builds a hypothesis around the data in an attempt to account for the effect in terms of selection pressures (e.g. food availability, predators, kin selection). As new data becomes available, the hypothesis is modified in an *ad hoc* manner to take account of the new facts. The difficulty of this 'after the event' approach is that the mind is flexible enough to construct a good story to 'explain' almost anything. Witness the rash of popular books speculating on the evolution of man's social life, and the ease with which alternative theories can be woven around the same evidence. The second, and more scientific, approach is to formulate hypotheses that lead to clear predictions which can be tested by further observation and experiment. This is illustrated below, with hypotheses relating predation to group size or the position of a nest in a colony. The extent to which these hypotheses rely on the evidence in hand or on theoretical predictions, will depend on the circumstances. This approach is more demanding as it is hard to collect the relevant data in the field and conclusive experiments are difficult to arrange.

The importance of studying individual differences in behaviour   If we wish to study natural selection we must concentrate on the variation between individuals (Chapter 2). The significance of differences in behaviour between individuals must therefore be studied. In every case we must ask how the behaviour affects the performer's fitness. Does it increase the chance that the performer's genes will be represented in the next generation, by comparison with others who show different behaviour? With promiscuous and long-lived animals, like many primates, it is difficult to measure an individual's contribution to the next generation and there has therefore been a tendency to guess the effect of a behaviour on fitness. This is best avoided. With promiscuous males the observer is often reduced to scoring copulation rates, a measure of unknown validity; for females, there is less of a problem since the number of young produced can be counted. In monogamous birds several estimates such as clutch size, hatching success and fledgling success are readily available and applicable to both sexes. With all of these estimates of fitness based on reproduction, it should not be forgotten that the important factor is *life-time reproductive success* (i.e. the number of mature, reproducing individuals the animal contributes to the next generation). This is usually impossible to measure. Other estimates of fitness are of course available: when assessing the value of anti-predator strategies, the relative survival of individuals is used (see below). When investigating kin selection, the survival and reproductive success of relatives would be appropriate.

Individual differences in reproductive behaviour in kittiwakes   A study of the reproductive biology of kittiwakes illustrates the value of looking at individual differences in behaviour. These small gulls nest in colonies on cliffs and the central nesting sites in a colony are more attractive than peripheral sites. The males compete for the central sites and this therefore raises the question of whether centrally nesting males have a higher reproductive success than peripherally nesting males. In a long-term study of a colony that conveniently nests on the window ledges of a large warehouse, the birds were individually colour-ringed and their age, eggs and young recorded. The results showed that central males have a higher life-time reproductive success than peripheral males. This is due to a variety of factors. Central males (but not females) are significantly heavier (mean weight = 393.5 g versus 385.9 g), have a significantly lower mortality and live and breed longer (10 years breeding, versus 6). Central males change their mates less frequently, an important point because birds that keep the same mate produce more young than newly established pairs (Table 7). Interestingly, the success of new pairs depends on whether the new mate was taken because the previous one died, or because they 'divorced', the previous mate still living in the colony. Success also depends on the female's previous breeding experience; the more experienced birds do better on average. These factors all interact and have to be teased apart to reveal the long-term value of central nesting. The

Table 7 The mean number of young fledged per pair of kittiwakes according to the breeding experience of the female, pair status and position in the colony. Numbers in brackets are the sample size. (From COULSON, J. C. (1972). *Proc. 15th Int. Ornithological Cong.*, 424–33.)

| Pair status | Female's breeding experience (years) | | | | | |
| | *1* | | *2–4* | | *5–16* | |
	edge	centre	edge	centre	edge	centre
Breeding for the first time	1.16 (93)	1.06 (99)	—	—	—	—
Same mate	—	—	1.37 (64)	1.43 (83)	1.51 (74)	1.62 (150)
Divorced	—	—	1.23 (48)	1.31 (44)	1.34 (46)	1.47 (44)
Mate died	—	—	1.15 (26)	1.29 (16)	1.22 (19)	1.27 (24)

success of the central males probably depends on their ability to keep the same mate and to live longer. The figures in the table include data from when the colony was expanding. A subsequent analysis has shown that once the colony size had stabilized, the mortality of the central males increased to that of the peripheral males, perhaps because of the extra effort required to defend central nest sites.

8.1.2 Which selection pressures are important?

When these individual differences in social behaviour and fitness are found, the next step is to ask which selection pressures are acting on the animals to produce the differences. Selection pressures include environmental factors (e.g. predation and distribution, abundance and quality of food), social factors (e.g. population density and competition for mates) and other evolutionary forces such as kin selection. It must be recognized, however, that there will be an interaction between selection pressures. A male baboon could, for example, gain increased protection from predators by tolerating other adult males in his group, but only at the cost of losing some copulations to them and of increased competition for food. In some cases experimental work on selection pressures is possible, as discussed below.

Individual differences in predation When the size of fish shoals was increased from one to six to twenty individuals, it was found that predatory pike (*Esox lucius*) and perch (*Perca fluviatilis*) became less successful. The relationship between nest position and predation in a colony of black-headed gulls has also been investigated experimentally. Hens' eggs (which the gulls do not eat), were laid out 10 m apart in lines at right angles with the colony edge. Each line was half inside and half outside the colony. As predatory carrion crows (*Corvus corone*) approached, they were mobbed by the gulls and the experimental eggs inside the colony survived longer than those outside: before the birds arrived at the colony site for breeding there was no difference in survival. These results illustrate one of the advantages of colonial nesting and in fact gulls that nest outside the main colony rear few or no young. Paradoxically, the clumping of gull nests together makes them easier for the predators to find but this disadvantage is outweighed by mutual defence and other factors. In some species the balance tips the other way and solitary nesting results.

In some cases, experimental manipulation may be unnecessary since the observer can exploit natural differences between individuals. Caution is required, however, since in nature there may be additional unknown differences between individuals (e.g. age or breeding experience). It could, for example, be asked whether the spacing out of great tit nests, resulting from territorial behaviour, reduces nest predation. Imagine nests packed closely together as in the gull example above. Once a predator finds one he could easily find another; with well-spaced nests this would be less likely. In fact the probability of predation falls significantly as the distance between nest increases (Fig. 8–1). Predation pressure may therefore be one factor that makes territoriality adaptive for great tits. It is unlikely to be the only factor (see § 8.5), just as predation is unlikely to be the only selection pressure producing fish shoaling or colonial nesting in birds.

Evolutionary constraints   When judgements are made about the adaptive significance of an animal's behaviour, this is often done with reference to

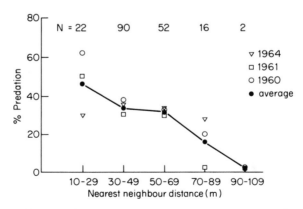

Fig. 8–1   Predation and nest-spacing in great tits. Percentage predation (mainly by weasels) at different distances from nearest neighbouring nest. Data from three years of high nesting density, predation is proportionally more severe at these times. N = total number of nests on which each average point is based. (From KREBS, J. R. (1971). *Ecology*, **52**, 1–22.)

its current environment. It should be remembered, however, that each animal carries to the present time features that evolved during the species' past history and which must constrain future evolutionary change. There are, of course, no fossil records of behaviour or selection pressures and it is therefore difficult to determine the course of behavioural evolution. The one technique that is available is to compare the behaviour of species that are known from other evidence to be closely related. Thus, most of the related group of monkeys comprising the baboons, macaques and mangabeys have superficially similar multi-male societies, even though they live in widely different habitats ranging from dry savanna to tropical forest and temperate woodland. It is reasonable to conclude, therefore, that their society type owes much to their past history. When one looks at the species in finer detail, however, behaviour differences do come to light that are related to the current environment.

8.2   Some advantages of social life

We can now further examine the main advantages of being social. A word of caution is, however, pertinent before we start: take care when generalizing from one species to another because of the great diversity of animal structure, social life and environments.

8.2.1   Protection from predators

Most animals are subject to predation and many aspects of social life appear to be anti-predator strategies. Birds foraging in open habitats need to keep a sharp look out for predators. The time spent eating must be balanced with the time spent avoiding being eaten. Many birds solve this problem by living in groups and gaining from the vigilance of their fellows. Thus, as group size increases, the proportion of time each individual spends looking around falls, but the total number of vigilant birds increases (Fig. 8–2). Response time to predators also falls as flock size increases. This was shown by flying a stuffed hawk over captive feeding groups of one, five or ten starlings. Groups of ten reacted significantly faster (mean = 3.2 s) and with less variation (standard deviation (SD) ± 0.58) than single birds (mean = 4.1 s, SD ± 0.95). With increasing group size from one to five to ten, each animal spent a smaller percentage of its foraging time being vigilant (47 to 30 to 12%) and its frequency of vigilance fell (0.39 to 0.30 to 0.19 s⁻¹). The significance of this experiment is clear; each member of the flock gains from the vigilance of others.

Fish, birds and monkeys often close ranks when a predator appears. This has long been assumed to make them harder to catch, because their rapid movement within a confined space would make it difficult for a predator to single out a target. Evidence is rare, but the fish experiments referred to above (p. 77) showed that as shoal size increased, a higher

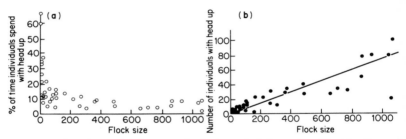

Fig. 8–2   The relationship between flock size and vigilance in wild white-fronted geese (*Anser albifrons*). When not in the head-up posture the birds are feeding, with head down. (a) Percentage of time individuals spend with head up. The open circles on the ordinate represent solitary birds. (b) Number of individuals with head up. The straight line has been fitted by eye. (After DIMOND, S. and LAZARUS, J. (1974). *Brain, Behaviour and Evolution*, 9, 60–79. S. Karger, A.G. Basel.)

proportion of the predators' attacks failed. Crowding also probably occurs because it is to each individual's advantage to get to the centre of the group and so place others between itself and the predator. Even birds which do not live in groups may temporarily band together to mob a predator: chaffinches and other small passerines mob owls and birds of prey. Mobbing succeeds because it advertises the predator's presence, lets it know that it has been spotted and, by depriving it of an element of surprise, makes it better for it to hunt elsewhere. As the predator is deprived of surprise attacks, mobbing presumably involves little risk.

The risks that an animal takes in response to predators depend on several factors: the probability of being killed or maimed, whether its young need protection, how easily its young can be replaced and, if the animals being protected are not offspring, their genetic relatedness to the protector. For example, the self-sacrificing behaviour of social Hymenoptera defending their colony, must be linked to the high degree of relatedness between colony members (p. 13).

8.2.2   Feeding efficiency

As already shown, birds can feed more efficiently by reducing the risk of predation. Feeding efficiency can, however, be increased more directly. When food supplies are plentiful, small, dispersed and relatively stable in time (as for example is the case with the great tits' insect food in woodland during the early summer), individuals can forage effectively on their own. When food supplies are, however, clumped (i.e. lots of food in a few places, none in many others), the foragers face real problems in finding food. One way to overcome these is for unsuccessful birds to exploit successful birds by following them to food. Experiments with captive great tits have shown that once one bird finds food, other flock members change their searching behaviour and look in the same area and type of place in which the food was found. During one experiment single great tits found food in only 6/24 tests, but when the same birds were tested in groups of four, 18/24 were successful. Winter-flocking by great tits (p. 35) may therefore benefit the individual by increasing its chances of finding food.

Similar arguments can sometimes be applied to the evolution of colonial nesting and roosting. The colonial nest site of the great blue heron may act as an 'information centre'. These birds feed on fish that occur in shoals at unpredictable locations in tidal pools. A feeding bird soon attracts others (this was shown experimentally by putting out decoys), birds from neighbouring nests tend to feed in the same places and may follow each other to feed, and a bird feeding in a flock of 20 gets about five times as much food per minute as a solitary bird.

Carnivores such as spotted hyaenas, lions, hunting dogs and wolves hunt cooperatively to catch large prey. Lions hunt by stalking, ambush and brief spurts of running, while the others rely on out-running and cooperatively overwhelming the prey. With hyaenas, the prey species can be predicted from the numbers of individuals present: a wildebeest hunt is started by one to three hyaenas with others arriving later to join in the kill, but before hunting zebras, the hyaenas form a group averaging 11 animals. These differences are adaptive: apart from a mother helping her young, wildebeest put up no cooperative defence but more hyaenas are required to neutralize the kicking and biting of the zebra stallions which defend their groups.

8.2.3 Reproductive efficiency

Although the evolution of parental behaviour in general has been discussed (Chapter 2), it is now necessary to consider why males play such different parts in different societies (p. 21). A female's reproductive output is limited to the number of eggs she can make or brood, or the young that she can suckle. A male's potential output is larger: sperm are produced in millions and numerous copulations are possible. In some environments, however, it is very difficult for a female to rear young on her own and under these conditions it is clearly advantageous for the male to stay to help: males who fertilize lots of females but do not stay to help will leave few young. The males may be needed for protection (zebras and baboons), or to assist in food-collecting (great tits and foxes). In territorial species, the male's role starts well before the young are born. He plays the major part in obtaining resources by defending a nest site or an area in which food can be found. When a male's help is not needed, males tend to be promiscuous because sexual selection (p. 12) favours males who can achieve as many matings as possible. Promiscuity is particularly likely if the young can feed themselves soon after birth (as in many game birds such as the black grouse), or if the male's ability to feed the young is severely limited (as in mammals). Another aspect of this story

– why some males are polygynous with a harem of females – is taken up below.

8.2.4   Division of labour

The different members of a society often specialize in their behaviour and so increase the society's efficiency, to their individual advantage. The different emphasis between the sexes in territorial behaviour and the changing duties of worker honeybees, have already been mentioned.

8.2.5   Cultural evolution

When there is an overlap of generations the transmission of behaviour by learning from one generation to another becomes possible, as previously illustrated by the cultural transmission of chaffinch song dialects (p. 70). A further example is provided by Japanese macaques in which new behaviour patterns have been produced experimentally. These animals have a rich repertoire of vocal and other behaviour patterns and eat a very varied diet. Detailed study has revealed natural inter-population differences in all of these features (for example, in the extent that males care for infants) and these may be transmitted by learning. The acquisition of new feeding habits has been studied by giving the macaques new foods. Sweet-eating, sweet-potato-washing, digging for peanuts in sand and placer-mining of wheat grains (i.e. throwing a mixture of grain and sand into water so as to collect the floating grain), all spread from juveniles to age-peers and mothers, and from mothers to infants. The sub-adult and adult males, who have little interaction with juveniles, are the least likely to learn. Two of these patterns – sweet-potato-washing and placer-mining – were invented by a particularly innovative juvenile female. Once in use the behaviour patterns were slowly modified. The animals changed from washing potatoes in fresh water to using sea water (for the seasoning effect of salt?) and modified the hand movements used to clean the potatoes. The use of the sea for food preparation was eventually followed by juveniles learning to swim and even to dive for seaweed! These examples demonstrate a vast latent capacity for cultural evolution and illustrate, in contrast with genetic evolution, its potential speed.

Evidence of another sort for cultural evolution in animals is seen in the many species in which traditional roosting and breeding sites are found. Seal colonies, rookeries and heronies have existed in the same place for generations, as have bird roosts and the calving grounds of reindeer. In many cases there appear to be alternative sites available, but it is presumably adaptive for an individual to keep to traditional sites, since these are proven to be suitable and they also offer the guarantee that other members of the species will be present.

Compared with the complexity of human culture, with its dependence on the written and spoken word, the cultural transmission of behaviour in animals may seem trivial but it perhaps suggests how human culture may have started.

8.3   The inevitability of social competition

The consequences of social life are not always so beneficial as might be inferred from the previous discussion. As would be expected from a knowledge of the mechanisms of evolution, competition between individuals is inevitable. There will often be insufficient resources (e.g. nesting sites, mates) to go around and even if these are abundant, competition can be expected for the best (e.g. prime habitat, best mates). Some individuals – the high-ranking ones – are obviously going to do better than others.

8.3.1   Competitive strategies and their benefits and costs

As a general rule, the effort an individual puts into a competitive situation and the risks it takes when fighting are proportional to its potential loss, if it loses, and its gains, if it wins. Animals like male red grouse, which are as good as dead if they do not get a territory (see p. 11), are playing for 'big stakes' and can be expected to compete hard. On the other hand, consider a relatively long-lived animal such as a male macaque who is competing for females within his group: if he is young and has little success he can bide his time and try later. Such an animal would not be expected to risk all in an early push for success. This is, of course, an over-simplification but it does illustrate that there are a variety of competitive strategies. The most successful of these will be perpetuated in subsequent generations, a point that applies equally well to individuals who do not obtain the best resources. Thus, great tits who fail to get woodland territories do not give up, they occupy hedgerows where they can still breed but with less success. In a social group, a low-ranking animal tends to stay in the group rather than leave to join another. These are presumably the best strategies to adopt under the circumstances. Another strategy, which occurs when close relatives live together, is for an unsuccessful animal to aid the reproduction of a relative. This is what would be predicted from the theory of kin selection.

8.3.2   The advantages of high rank and the disadvantages of low rank

Sexual selection (p. 12) is so important that competition for mates predominates in many social organizations, high-ranking animals generally fathering most young. Sexual selection can also act after birth. When the single male is ousted from a langur harem or the males are ousted from a lion pride, the suckling young are often killed by the invading male(s). Having lost their young, the females become receptive and the new male fathers young of his own. There are other resources besides mates at stake within societies, and animals may compete for food, resting places, grooming partners and so on. In many instances, dominant–subordinate relationships are established and actual fighting over resources may be infrequent. It is often said that the function of a social hierarchy is to reduce fighting and to preserve peace. This is an incorrect way of looking at the problem. A hierarchy does not exist as a discrete entity (p. 60) and can therefore have no function as such. The predictability of the social relationships which we summate into a hierarchy, is the result of individuals adopting strategies to maximize their fitness, or to minimize their loss of fitness when at a disadvantage in a competitive situation. We see a hierarchy because the animals' relationships have become predictable, not vice versa.

At times of hardship, low-ranking animals are at a disadvantage and suffer a higher mortality. They will be in poorer physiological condition through being excluded from resources and because of the debilitating effects of the aggression they receive. For example, in rodents (such as house-mice, and wood-mice), high competition resulting from high population density, often lowers reproductive success. Reduced fertility, embryonic reabsorption and litter mortality through disturbance, can all be implicated (see DELANY, 1974). Low-ranking animals are often forced to migrate. In territorial systems, the position of the boundaries and territory size are the result of the establishment of an equilibrium between the behaviour of neighbours. When population density is high and competition intense, territories may be relatively small. There is, however, a lower limit to territory size and some animals may not get territories. This can limit the number of animals breeding in an area.

8.4   The adaptive nature of social organization
8.4.1   Investigating the evolution of social organization

When discussing the evolution of social organization it is usual to refer to the adaptive significance of different *patterns* of social organization. Such a statement, however, implies acceptance of the theory of population selection. This is because certain aspects of a social system (e.g. social competition) may be disadvantageous to some individuals. To state that the whole pattern of social organization is adaptive can give the impression that such individuals have been selected to act for the good of the group or species. Any comments on adaptation must, in this context, refer to individuals.

Unfortunately, investigating the adaptive significance of individual differences in behaviour (as described earlier) can be extremely difficult. Because of this, another approach has developed. This relies on examining differences in social organization within and between species and on investigating the relationship between the environment, social organization and anatomical traits such as body weight, size and sexual dimorphism. Since social organization is a complex phenomenon,

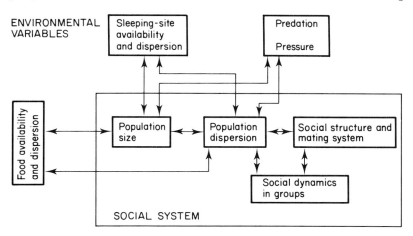

Fig. 8–3 The interaction between environmental variables and aspects of a primate social system. Environmental variables (shown outside the large box) interact, as indicated by the arrows, with social system variables (shown inside the large box), and vice versa. The social system variables also interact with each other. For example, a change in predation pressure may influence population size and population dispersion, which may then influence food availability and dispersion, and the dynamics of social behaviour in groups. (From CROOK, J. H. (1970). In: Crook, J. H. (Ed.) *Social Behaviour in Birds and Mammals*. Academic Press, London, 103–66.)

particular attention must be paid to the inevitable interaction between its components and between them and the environment (Fig. 8–3).

Social organization often appears to be matched to the environment. A feeling that this is so is reinforced when it is found that related species living in contrasting habitats, or exploiting a single habitat in different ways, have social organizations that 'make sense' in relation to the conditions under which they live. Many aspects of the social organization of spotted hyaenas are related to their hunting large prey such as zebra and wildebeest. By contrast, the striped hyaena (*Hyaena vulgaris*) feeds on much smaller prey and shows related differences in hunting behaviour, population dispersion and social communication (Table 8).

8.4.2 Comparing the social organization of common and sacred baboons

Further insights are provided by comparing the social organization of baboons. Common baboons have multi-male groups (p. 36) while the closely related sacred baboon has a quite different social structure: adult males have harems of two to five adult females and their young (Fig. 8–4). These harems are quite discrete; apart from play interactions among the young they do not mix. The harem male herds his females and trains them

Table 8   Some aspects of the behaviour of spotted and striped hyaenas. (After KRUUK, H. (1975). In: *Function and Evolution of Behaviour*, G. Baerends; C. Beer and A. Manning (eds). Clarendon Press, Oxford, 119–41.)

Behaviour	Spotted hyaena	Striped hyaena
Gregariousness	Multi-male societies (clans)	Family units
Main food	Large or small ungulates	Carrion, insects, fruits
Foraging strategy	Clan splits into solitary individuals or temporary groups for social hunting	Solitary searching
Land tenure	Clan territory (group defence)	Large individual territory
Parental organization	Many females in one den; 2 cubs per litter; no food brought to cubs; male not involved	One female per den; 3–4 cubs per litter; male and female bring food to cubs
Vocalizations	Varied, loud, frequent; has long-range call	Rare; no long-range call
Displays	Many tail and genital displays	Few tail and no genital displays

to stay with him by biting them on the neck if they stray. A young male, called a 'follower', is sometimes attached to a harem but such males have no sexual access to the females. Many of the younger males, and some adult males, are, however, completely excluded from the harems. Several harems that regularly associate together make a 'band' of up to 90 animals; this can be considered equivalent to a common baboon group. Sacred baboons live in the semi-deserts of Ethiopia and Arabia – a much poorer habitat than that occupied by common baboons. Sleeping sites are rare and at night several bands aggregate together on rocky outcrops.

These differences in the social organization of baboons have been related to their contrasting environments. It is argued that common baboons live in areas of high predation and have evolved large groups containing several adult males for protection. Sacred baboons live in areas of lower predation where such cooperative protection is not required. Smaller groups are essential because in the semi-desert food is scarce, scattered and insufficient to feed large groups, while the converse is true of the common baboons' environment. So far, our discussion has centred on the relationship between social organization and the environment, but other factors are also important. In the present context the sacred baboons' habitat may explain why they forage in small groups but the fact that these are harems can be attributed to sexual selection. A harem male can keep his females from mating with other males and prevent the latter from directly competing for food with the females and young. The males' magnificent capes (Fig. 8–4) can probably be attributed to intrasexual selection. Arguments of this sort are quite

Fig. 8–4   Sacred baboons. Three harem-owning males, with capes of long hair, are shown with their attendant females and young. (From KUMMER, H. (1968). *Social Organization of Hamadryas Baboons*. Karger, Basel.)

plausible, but note that many of the ecological assumptions need to be substantiated.

8.4.3   Comparing the social organization of colobus monkeys

Early attempts to understand the diversity of primate social organization relied on large ecological and social categories which are now known to be inadequate. Within any one habitat there are numerous ecological niches and it is necessary to study the adaption to these. For example, the black and white colobus monkey (*Colobus guereza*) eats leaves while a closely related species in the same forest, the red colobus (*C. badius*) has a broader diet of fruit, flowers, leaves and shoots. Such differences in diet can have a profound influence on social organization. As leaves are available in large quantities and since they can live on mature leaves when necessary, the black and white colobus can find their food in small areas (0.2 km²) that are defensible as territories by small groups of 5–10 animals. The food supply of the red colobus is less stable and they must utilize more tree species so that some always have fresh shoots, flowers or fruits. To get access to the variety of trees needed they tend to live in larger ranges (1 km²) in the wetter parts of the forest. They live in large groups of 40 or more individuals, either for protection from predatory chimpanzees, to aid food-finding, or perhaps because small groups simply could not defend an area sufficiently large to contain the necessary resources.

8.4.4   Other types of evidence

It has only been possible to examine two cases of interspecific differences in primate social organization. To discover whether there are any general principles it is necessary to look systematically at the relationship between relevant variables in numerous species. One such analysis, based on 100 species, revealed a positive relationship between home-range area and the biomass of primate groups and, as already suggested by the *Colobus* example above, for a given group weight fruit-eaters have larger home ranges than leaf-eaters (Fig. 8–5).

Particularly convincing evidence for environmental effects on social organization can be expected from comparative studies of different populations of the same species. If differences in social organization correlate with environmental differences, then this may suggest which ecological selection pressures are important: the phylogenetic basis for any differences will be minimal. Under very harsh conditions common baboons tend to forage in small sub-groups of three to four animals, in contrast to the cohesive large groups found in savanna and forest. Average home ranges are also smaller in forest (5 km² in contrast to

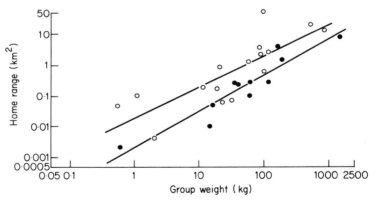

Fig. 8–5   The relationship between home range size (km²) and the biomass of the social group (kg) for different primate genera. Although there is obviously variability, for a given group weight fruit eaters (o, upper line) have larger ranges than leaf eaters (●, lower line). Note that the scales are logarithmic. Examples of fruit eaters: baboon, chimpanzee, macaque, gibbon, cebus monkey (e.g. *Cebus apella*), squirrel monkey (e.g. *Saimiri sciureus*). Examples of leaf eaters: gorilla (*Gorilla gorilla beringei*), langur, colobus, howling monkey. (After CLUTTON-BROCK, T. H. and HARVEY, P. H. (1977). *J. Zool. Lond.*, **183**, 1–39.)

perhaps 40 km² in savanna), average densities are higher (8 km⁻² versus 4 km⁻²) and day ranges in search of food shorter. There are also differences in social behaviour: less overt agonistic behaviour occurs in forest and agonistic hierarchies are absent or difficult to discern.

8.5   Why be territorial?

Although it is only part of the general problem of understanding the evolution of social organization, it is useful to take a special look at why some animals are territorial when others are not. The dispersion patterns seen in nature (and the relationship between territory and home range) were discussed earlier (p. 27).

8.5.1   Territories and their function

There is no single function of territoriality: many functions have been suggested and each case must be interpreted separately.

Nesting territories   Some territories – *nesting territories* – are extremely small and are used solely for the nest, courtship, copulation and rearing. The examples already discussed include the black-headed gull and kittiwake, but it is a general phenomenon in colonially nesting birds. Territorial ownership ensures a nest site in the colony and all the advantages that this provides. Neighbours eventually accept each other's rights, intruders are relatively easily evicted and breeding can take place, presumably with less disturbance than if there was a continuous 'free-for-all'. In some species the territory may even protect young from cannibalism – lesser black-backed gull chicks (*Larus fuscus*) are quite safe on their parents' territory but if they wander outside, they may quickly be eaten by other colony members.

Mating territories   Other animals, particularly birds (e.g. black grouse and ruffs (*Philomachus pugnax*)) establish small *mating territories* on leks; food and shelter are found elsewhere. Lek males display and fight amongst themselves, the most successful obtain central territories, attract most females and do most mating (p. 23). Whatever the species, lek males are promiscuous, do not form pair-bonds and play no part in rearing young. Such a system could only evolve if the young can be reared without the male's assistance. Freed from these responsibilities, intense intrasexual selection is inevitable and the males evolve their marked nuptial plumages and displays. From a male's point of view, if he wins a place on the lek and dominates other males, then this advertises his worth. The concentration of displaying males may also make them more obvious and attractive to females than males displaying on their own. Although female black grouse tend to visit several displaying males before copulating, the prolonged courtship displays seen in most non-lek species are not required to test the male's quality. A female can be sure of a good mate by choosing a male who has obtained a central territory by dominating its rivals.

General purpose territories   Nesting and mating territories are rather special cases. More frequently *general purpose* territories are seen, as described earlier for gibbons, great tits and robins. These are of course larger and usually contain most or all of the resources necessary for reproduction.

8.5.2   *The evolution of territoriality*

We must now answer the question: why do some animals have general purpose territories, while others have overlapping non-exclusive home ranges? This is an evolutionary question and can be approached by seeking the relationship between individual differences in behaviour and fitness. For territoriality to evolve it is assumed that, all other things being equal, territorial individuals have a higher reproductive success. To understand the evolution of territoriality three features must be investigated: (i) the cost of territorial behaviour; (ii) whether any resources are in short supply (and hence the source of competition); and (iii) their 'economic defensibility' (Fig. 8–6).

The costs of territorial behaviour   Territorial behaviour can be very costly. This seems a reasonable assumption in view of the time and energy put into displays and advertisement by song and scent. Territorial behaviour involves aggression which, in spite of the ritualized nature of many displays, still carries a risk of injury. For an animal to accept these costs there must be compensatory benefits or there would be selection against territoriality.

Sources of competition   Territorial defence implies that there is something to defend against competition from other individuals. Otherwise, why should an animal attempt to take over a defended resource if the equivalent is undefended and available nearby? The fact

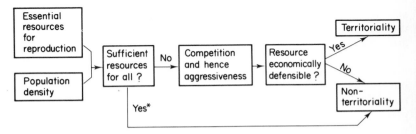

Fig. 8–6 A general model of the evolution of diversity in intraspecific population dispersion systems. The link marked '*' would be unstable since it would probably lead to a rapid increase in population density and hence insufficient resources.

that competition occurs, implies that the basic resource is in short supply, or that there are considerable differences in resource quality which make the higher quality resources worth disputing. The resources might, according to the species or situation, be food (in the case of gibbons and red grouse), nesting sites (kittiwakes, gannets) or more simply 'space', if the spacing-out of nests, for example, reduces the chance of predation (great tits) or minimizes the chance of other males copulating with the territory owner's mate. In the case of general purpose territories it is, however, often difficult to know which is the key resource. For example, the fact that an animal finds food for its family in its territory does not prove that food is the source of competition.

Economic defensibility   Given that there is a source of competition, the final factor that determines whether territorial defence occurs is probably the economic defensibility of the resource. When food density is high and distributed in a relatively even and stable pattern, the area required to support each individual is small. Thus the breeding song bird or gibbon in a good habitat needs only a small area to provide for its family. Small areas can be defended with minimum energy costs, and because the area is small, intruders are easily noticed and chased off. When resources are more widely spaced and unpredictable, each individual needs a larger area to support itself. When animals must live in large groups for other reasons (e.g. because of predation) the total group range can be very large – for example, up to 40 km^2 in common baboons. Such an area clearly cannot be economically defended. The boundaries are enormous, patrolling them would leave little time for anything else and intruders could easily slip in and out unnoticed. It is not surprising that under these conditions home ranges overlap extensively and are undefended. A similar argument can be developed for colonial sea birds – a nesting site is defensible, but the surrounding sea, in which food is found, is not.

References and Further Reading

ARCHER, J. (1979). *Animals Under Stress.* Studies in Biology, no. 108. Edward A
London.
BASTOCK, M. (1967). *Courtship. A Zoological Study.* Heinemann, London.
BROWN, J. L. (1975). *The Evolution of Behaviour.* Norton, New York.
CARTHY, J. D. (1979). *The Study of Behaviour.* Second edition. Revised by HOW
Studies in Biology, no. 3. Edward Arnold, London.
DELANY, M. J. (1974). *The Ecology of Small Mammals.* Studies in Biology, 1
Edward Arnold, London.
EDWARDS, K. J. R. (1977). *Evolution in Modern Biology.* Studies in Biology, 1
Edward Arnold, London.
FREE, J. B. (1977). *The Social Organization of Honeybees.* Studies in Biology, 1
Edward Arnold, London.
HINDE, R. A. (1974). *Biological Bases of Human Social Behaviour.* McGraw-Hil
York.
JEEVES, M. (1974). *Experimental Psychology. An Introduction for Biologists.* Stu
Biology, no. 47. Edward Arnold, London.
MANNING, A. (1979). *An Introduction to Animal Behaviour.* 3rd edition. E
Arnold, London.
MESSENGER, J. B. (1979). *Nerves, Brains and Behaviour.* Studies in Biology, no
Edward Arnold, London.
ROWELL, T. E. (1972). *Social Behaviour of Monkeys.* Penguin, Harmondsworth.
SLATER, P. J. B. (1978). *Sex Hormones and Behaviour.* Studies in Biology, no
Edward Arnold, London.
SMITH, J. M. (1975). *The Theory of Evolution.* 3rd edition. Penguin, Harmonds
SOLOMON, M. E. (1976). *Population Dynamics.* 2nd edition. Studies in Biology, 1
Edward Arnold, London.
STODDART, D. M. (1976). *Mammalian Odours and Pheromones.* Studies in Bi
no. 73. Edward Arnold, London.
TINBERGEN, N. (1964). *Social Behaviour in Animals.* Chapman and Hall, Londo
TINBERGEN, N. (1974). *Curious Naturalists.* Revised edition. Penguin, Harm
worth.
WILSON, E. O. (1975). *Sociobiology.* Belknap Press, Cambridge, Massachusetts.
WOOD-GUSH, D. G. M. (1971). *The Behaviour of Domestic Fowl.* Heinemann, Lon

**Books and articles that include practical exercises on social behaviour or
on methodology.**

ALTMANN, J. (1974). Observational study of behaviour: sampling me
Behaviour, **49,** 227–67.
EVANS, S. M. (1970). *The Behaviour of Birds, Mammals and Fish.* Heinemann, Lo
HANSELL, M. H. and AITKEN, J. J. (1977). *Experimental Animal Behaviour.* B
Glasgow.
HINDE, R. A. (1973). On the design of check-sheets. *Primates,* **14** (4), 393–406.
McBRIDE, G. (1976). The study of social organizations. *Behaviour,* **59,** 96–115.
STOKES, A. W. (Ed.) (1968). *Animal Behaviour in Laboratory and Field.* W. H. Fre
San Francisco. (There is an accompanying teacher's manual.)
TINBERGEN (1964). Listed above; see Chapter 9, *Some Hints for Research in A
Sociology.*